chic & slim

TECHNIQUES

Nº 1

The Anne Barone Company
P.O. Box 3241, Wichita Falls TX 76301

Website: annebarone.com

ISBN: 0-9658943-6-3

A NOUVELLES EDITIONS BOOK
Published by The Anne Barone Company

First Edition

Printed in the United States of America
at Morgan Printing in Austin, Texas

Book & Cover Design: Anne Barone
Eiffel Tower Design: Joyce Wells GriggsArt
Cover Photo: Anne Barone August 2002

Printing 10 9 8 7 6 5 4 3 2 1

chic & slim

TECHNIQUES

N° 1

10 techniques to make you
chic & slim
à la française

Anne Barone

NOUVELLES EDITIONS

more *chic & slim* by

anne barone

chic & slim:
how those chic French women
eat all that rich food
and still stay slim

chic & slim Encore
more about how
French women
dress chic stay slim
—and how you can too!

annebarone.com
chic & slim le website

chic & slim

TECHNIQUES
N° 1

CONTENTS

Bonjour! - 8

What's the Difference?

Don't you just hate it?

You buy and love a book by an author and you want more information on the subject. You buy a second book, and for all practical purposes, it is just the book you have already read with a different cover and a little additional new material. Very annoying.

Be assured that each *Chic & Slim* book is a new and different book. Of course all the *Chic & Slim* books deal with the same basic subject: how those chic French women manage their slim figures, chic personal style, and a happy and successful life — and how *you* can have a slim figure, chic personal style, and a happy and successful life *no matter where you live*. But the material discussing this subject in each book is at least 95% new. (A few things are so important that they do need to be repeated over and over.)

Chic & Slim Encore was written in response to the many requests from readers of the original *Chic & Slim*. These women (and a few men) wanted more information about how French women dress so chic, eat so well, and still stay so slim. Both *Chic & Slim* and *Chic & Slim Encore* are designed around six major chapters. Each chapter analyzes one of the six major factors that help chic French women eat that rich French food, yet stay slim: **Culture, Art of Being Women, Cuisine, Shopping & Decor, Relationships With Men,** and **Personal Style**.

The original *Chic & Slim* was designed to distill into 100 pages the French philosophy that allows those chic French women to eat so well and stay so slim. A kind of *hors d'oeuvre*.

Chic & Slim Encore, at twice the length of the original book, is more substantial, more a main course. The third book, the *Chic & Slim Techniques* book, was designed to help you discard those attitudes and practices that prevent you from being as chic, slim, and successful as you would like and achieve those French attitudes and practices that give French women that envied *je ne sais quoi*.

Chic & Slim Techniques gives you recipes for your chic & slim success. The book will enable you to achieve this success *à la française* even when you lack the time or money to go to France and observe the French system firsthand.

Should you read all three books? *Mais oui!*

Bonjour!

French women are made, not born.

Parisian-born Véronique Vienne assures us of this fact in her wonderful book *French Style*.

So if French women achieve their chic style, slim figures, serene self-confidence, their femininity and mystique by deliberate effort, then can't any woman acquire that alluring French *je ne sais quoi* if she has a few well-designed techniques to help her?

I believe that any woman, whatever her nationality, wherever she lives, can do just that.

In my two previous *Chic & Slim* books, and on the *Chic & Slim* website, *annebarone.com,* I share with you what I have learned over the past three decades about how those chic French women achieve their chic style and stay slim. Additionally, you may have read recent media articles about French success at chic and slim. If so, you probably have in mind ways in which you would like to be more like French women.

Surely we would all like to have French women's confidence and serenity. We would like to have a personal style as chic as French women do (on as little money!) and stay as slim while enjoying delicious real food. We would love to maintain the healthy food and lifestyle habits French women do. We would certainly like to maintain their elegant posture. We would love to be as feminine as those *ooh-la-la* French women and enjoy those satisfying relationships with men that make French women's efforts to appear attractive so worthwhile. And we would love to have their aura of mystery, their legendary French mystique that others find so mesmerizing.

No French woman considers herself "finished" before she is 30. Until then, she is a work-in-progress. She is an artist, and she is creating a special work of art: herself. The process she begins as a girl takes years to complete. But years! *Mais non!* We want our changes for success in much less time!

Designing techniques that will enable you, no matter where you live, to jettison defeating habits and attitudes and replace them with those habits and attitudes you admire in French women *in as little time as possible* is the goal I set for myself when I wrote this book *Chic & Slim Techniques*.

One woman who read the first two *Chic & Slim* books emailed that she was a "long way from being French." Perhaps, with these techniques to speed the process along, you aren't as far as you might think from achieving French chic and slim— and a happy and successful lifestyle.

With these techniques, you may reach your goals in very little time. *Tout de suite!*

So put on your beret (if only in your imagination) set your lips in a seductive French pout, and begin using these techniques to create for yourself a chic style and a slim body *à la française.*

Anne Barone

chic & slim Technique 1
SABRINA

French culture, as well as their chic French mothers, aunts, and grandmothers serving as role models, help French women develop lifestyles and personal style that make them chic, slim, healthy and confident.

American women grow up in a Puritanical culture, often without good role models of happy and successful women. To develop into chic, slim, healthy, and confident women, they must make a dedicated effort to develop their unique personal styles and lifestyles.

This technique is designed to help you easily and quickly banish attitudes or beliefs that stand in the way of your success at becoming chic, slim, healthy, happy, and confident.

➤〜

The Sabrina Technique
THE NEW CHIC & SLIM YOU TECHNIQUE

Sabrina. She was the unattractive, insecure chauffeur's daughter (of the Broadway play and later two Hollywood films) who, with lessons she learned in Paris, returned home changed into a chic, confident, beautiful young woman who captured the millionaire tycoon's heart. But even if you never set foot in France, the French have good lessons for us, just as they had for Sabrina. To learn these useful lessons, you must make a dedication to change. And you must be willing to put out some effort to achieve your success.

Change requires not just effort, but intelligent effort. Often those efforts are attacked by others who do not wish us to succeed. Sometimes we sabotage them ourselves without realizing it. Deep in our subconscious, many of us have resistance to positive changes that have developed as a result of unfortunate experiences in our lives. How do we insure successful permanent change against the odds that improvements face?

In the 1954 version of *Sabrina*, there is a scene in which Audrey Hepburn as Sabrina is seen sitting at her little desk in her Paris apartment writing her father as she is preparing to return to the USA after finishing her cooking course. She tells her father that in France she has learned more important things than how to prepare French cuisine. "I have learned how to live. How to be in the world, and of the world. And not just to stand aside and watch." And she declares that she will "never again run away from Life."

If you are overweight, or if you are dressing in a manner that makes you appear less attractive than you really are (or both), could it be that you are running away from Life and hiding beneath your excess flesh and your detracting clothes?

If you are using fat as a protection, what are you afraid of? If there is some trauma in the past, then there may be a valid reason for seeking this security. Some of us need our defenses. But if you are fearful of looking attractive, might not you find other ways of protecting yourself? I understand pepper spray is better than mace. Here in Texas where I live, we have a concealed weapons law and many women carry a gun in their purse.

To cope with less physical attacks, think of the haughty arrogance those chic French women project. Their attitude says "Approach me if you dare, and do so with respect and politeness." At the time of the death of Princess Margaret of Great Britain in February 2002, an article by Associated Press writer Audrey Woods recalled the Princess's "icy, acid drop stare" with which she could freeze anyone who crossed the line of reserve she set around herself.

Expect people to treat you with politeness and respect (I do) and they will be more likely to respond in that manner (they usually do).

Knowing your destination is one of the basic prerequisites for successful arrival. It's also useful to know precisely where you are when you start out. This next step is so basic that many of you who have read the two *Chic & Slim* books have probably already done it. If not, you should because it is essential. Even if you have already made your lists, read my cautions.

Keep a notepad around for a day or two and have headings

for two lists one for "old" and another for "new." Under "old," write down those defeating habits and attitudes that you want to get rid of. Some possibilities are eating quickly, grazing on food while preparing meals, and forgetting to check the backside in the mirror before going out the door (Oh! How it would improve the general aesthetic level of the USA if more people would do this), letting food pushers prompt you to eat food you have no real hunger for, and never taking time for yourself.

Under "new," you might list always sitting for meals, designating some daily boudoir time, regularly pressing clothes, getting to bed before midnight each night, or finding a new hairdresser for a chic haircut.

You can add and subtract from your list as days pass. If you have a computer, creating your lists in a word processing program can be convenient and time saving. And always keep in mind the practicalities. I can outline the most chic, elegant, slim body maintaining, intellectual lifestyle imaginable. The reality is that it is impossible to create and maintain that lifestyle here in a small North Texas city on the time and money that I currently have.

In designing your new lifestyle, remember the good example of the French women's practicality. The French women I have known through the years always seemed to excel at decorating their houses, dressing themselves, preparing meals and organizing entertainment, yet did not exceed the time and money they had available.

When you do begin to lose weight and improve your appearance, are you prepared for tacky statements from jealous family members and acquaintances? I don't say friends, because surely a "friend" would not make tacky, jealous statements about health improvements. Would they?

When I returned to my home town after my weight loss, some people, who had known me as a fatty, did not immediately recognize me. Others were effusive in their compliments and truly shared my joy that I had lost the fat I had struggled so unsuccessfully to shed as a child and teenager. But not everyone was nice. On that first trip home, I was standing in a downtown store chatting with a family friend when a woman who could always be depended on to insult you walked in. She looked me up and down from head to toe, my former size 18 plus body now fitting nicely in a size 5. "Hello, Anne," she said. "I see your face still breaks out."

I waited until she was out of earshot before I laughed. I had changed. But she had not.

Will you be able to laugh when you have lost eight of the 25 pounds your doctor has told you to lose, and this tacky coworker goes on for 10 minutes every morning saying how sick you look?

I suggest that in such a case, you tell her you are sick. Tell her you suffer from Barone's Syndrome. The symptoms of this condition are when you have made progress improving your health and some tacky and insecure person says you look sick. Then, mimicking the French actress Juliette Binoche in a scene from the film *The Incredible Lightness of Being*, you begin hopping from one foot to the other and in a gleeful, sing-song chant repeat, "You're jealous! You're jealous! Ha, ha, ha! You're jealous."

Living in less sophisticated societies around the world, I learned the value of ritual in reinforcing change. Coming of age ceremonies in Africa and elsewhere impress upon the mind of the young woman or man that they are no longer children but are ready for the responsibilities and prerogatives of adulthood.

Likewise, we can devise a ritual for impressing on our minds that we are giving up our defeating habits and attitudes and committing ourselves to replacing them with more beneficial habits and attitudes. On the *Chic & Slim* website not long ago, I recommend the garbage bag technique for getting rid of your guilt about eating foods that were not the best choice for your body. The idea is to write on slips of paper all the unfortunate food practices and incidents about which you feel guilty, put the slips of paper in a garbage bag, tie it up, march out to the dumpster , and throw the bag away. You should then have a sense of liberation from your guilt over this overeating. As I have written elsewhere, I believe that guilt about overeating is often as much responsible for gaining excess weight as the excess calories consumed. You can also use the garbage bag technique to symbolically rid yourself of defeating habits and attitudes.

Another technique to facilitate change is to take a French name for yourself. (Some of you already have French names so you would have to choose a *different* French name.) Maybe someone named Bobbie Jo who had already eaten a good supper would snack on a whole medium pizza and wash it down with 12 ounces of cola watching three hours of television in the evening. But would someone named Marie-Jeanne or Claire do such a thing? *Non, non, non! Pas possible!*

If you wanted to go to a bit of expense here to reinforce this new thinking about yourself, you might have a medallion made for your key chain engraved with the new name. Or a name plate or calling cards. Yet another technique I have used when I want to make positive changes for my life is that I write a magazine profile of the new me. I imagine that I am a magazine writer who interviews me at my home some time after I have discarded defeating behaviors or inefficient systems, or when a move or major life situation change has necessitated a revamp of my lifestyle. I write an article about my lifestyle as it is *after* the changes. This article includes somewhat detailed information on my personal style of dressing, the decor of my home, my daily routine, my exercise program, the meals I eat and at what time, the china and cutlery I use, the kind of music I listen to, the books I read, my pets, the videos I watch, my travel. This takes several hours over a period of days to write. This profile serves as a guideline for the changes that I am attempting to make. It puts the emphasis on the new positive lifestyle rather than on the former lifestyle that is no longer serving me well.

Originally when I began using this technique, I worked in longhand. Now I use a word processing program on computer. This makes it easy to pull the profile up on screen and read it (at least once a week) for reinforcement. It is also useful to keep a printout in a folder where you can pick it up and read it when you have a few spare moments. You might keep it by your phone so you can pick it up and read a paragraph or two when you are "on hold."

Keep your profile in a folder or looseleaf notebook. (Call it your Lifestyle Notebook.) You can include photos of role models, magazine pages of decor you like, related media articles, anything that gives reinforcement and definition to your goals for yourself. And please, please stick with positive models. No negative images.

If you have no time for writing a profile, talk to yourself as if being interviewed, and then respond. Try this while doing household chores, putting on makeup, or cooking.

Abandon any feelings of resentment that you might have. Life is not fair. Most of us were shortchanged in one department or another. Just about every woman in the world has better legs than mine. Despite staying slim and regular toning exercise, compared to the legs practically every other woman I see wearing shorts or short skirts, mine do not rate very well. (And since I am 58 at this writing, my legs are not likely to make any radical improvements, at least without medical assistance.) Just as I was proofing this technique, I glanced out the window and saw a woman I know is as old as I and who, I am pretty sure, has never done five minutes leg toning in her whole life. She was wearing short shorts and her legs look really great.

Here is my choice: I can spend time resenting this, agonize over the cosmic unfairness of it all. Or, I can pull on a pair of jeans that hide the worst of my leg imperfections and get on with my life. If I really want to do something about this, I can spend some money and have some "medical editing."

There are so many things that you can control and change to make your appearance more attractive and your life better. Concentrate on those. Do not waste time lamenting those things that you cannot change.

I like, use, and recommend Dr. Nathaniel Branden's self-esteem books as aids to making positive lifestyle changes. Dr. Branden also has a website *nathanielbranden.net* for those of you with Internet connections.

Another book that might be useful also has a supporting website. Debbie Ford's *The Secret of the Shadow* is supported by supplemental information on the author's website. A warning here. When I checked the website, the welcome message on *debbieford.com* began: "I trust that you have been guided here because you are ready to claim your greatness, your brilliance and your Divinity." Her book *The Secret of the Shadow* begins: "Imagine that you knew at birth that you were a master, that you were powerful beyond measure, that you possessed enormous gifts, and that all it would take to deliver your gifts to the world was your desire."

As a plain speaking Texan, I am not comfortable with the New Age language in which Debbie Ford presents her information. But I think her concept in *The Secret of the Shadow* of a tape playing over and over in our heads is a useful one for dealing with subconscious resistance to positive changes we wish to make. This mind tape tells us that we really aren't capable of succeeding at weight loss, or business, or love, that we are unattractive, or too old to still be attractive (try telling that one to a French woman!), that somehow we just are not good enough for whatever we are working toward.

Unconscious beliefs do exert control over our thoughts, words, and behaviors, especially spontaneous behaviors to a situation. In her book's Chapter 5 "Reclaiming Your Power," Debbie Ford takes on the problem of people seeing themselves as victims and the need for accepting responsibility for our own healing and change. A thought particularly worth remembering as you work toward changes in your own lifestyle is a statement Debbie Ford makes about her own life changes. "One day at a time, I took actions that were consistent with the person I wanted to be rather than the person I had been. "

Taking actions consistent with the new chic and slim person we want to be achieves powerful results. Any of us who have successfully let go of defeating habits have likely employed that technique. I still do on a regular basis. At least once a day. I stop myself and say: "What would a chic French woman do in this situation?"

Like so many of us, I have negative tapes playing in my mind telling me that I am not this, or not that, or that I am too this or too that for success in something. And sometimes those negative mind tapes set me on a path to a defeating action. But often I stop myself and think: Is this action or reaction one that is really the person I want to be, or is it the way I was programmed to act or react by the painful experiences in my life? By those painful experiences that made me a fatty and kept me fat for many years. If instead of a fatty growing up in the USA heartland, if I had grown up slim within the French culture and with family members who would have given me good examples and training in how to live successfully as a woman, would I react this way? "What would a chic French woman do?"

The good news is that after repeatedly taking the actions of the person you want to be rather than taking the actions of the person that you were, you begin more and more automatically to take the actions of that person you want to be. You become that new, changed person. Often now I stop and smile to myself realizing that the successful response I have just given to a situation was so-o-o-o French. *Fantastique!*

How You Do It For Chic & Slim Success:

➤ If you are afraid of becoming chic and slim, look for protections other than excess fat and unattractive personal style.

➤ Get a clear idea of the habits and attitudes you wish to discard. Make a list.

➤ Get a clear idea of the habits and attitudes you wish to acquire. Make a list.

➤ Design a ritual to say farewell to the "old you." The garbage bag technique is one possibility. Writing an obituary for the "old you" is another possibility.

➤ Make or purchase a token that you see often that will remind you of the new person you are becoming. Key chain medallion, name plate, business card.

➤ Take daily actions consistent with the chic and slim person you want to be.

➤ Ask yourself: "What would a chic French woman do in this situation?" Then do it.

chic & slim Technique 2
CLASSIQUE

French women find men potent inspiration to put forth the effort to eat moderately and nutritiously, to take care of the small details of personal maintenance, and to keep their bodies in good physical condition. About 8 percent of the French population are obese.

American women are told to stay slim and healthy "for themselves" or to improve their health. About 60 percent of the US population are overweight.

This technique will encourage you to use the satisfaction from demonstrations of male admiration to help you make the effort required to stay chic and slim.

>—

The Classique Technique
THE MEN-AS-INSPIRATION TECHNIQUE

What is classic? Why is this technique to show you the philosophy behind French women finding men useful motivation to dress chic and stay slim called The Classique Technique?

Dictionary definitions for classic include: belonging to the highest rank or class, serving as the established model or standard, having lasting significance or worth, enduring.

A classic holds its value over time; classic design is good and workable. Over time French women have found strong motivation to make the effort to care for themselves and to dress attractively in the attention and positive reaction that men give them for these efforts. And it is not only young French women who receive the rewards for their efforts.

In Dorothy Adelson's *Roughing It On The Rue de la Paix*, her book about her life in Paris, she tells of a party she attended there:

> A woman's taste in "arranging herself" was recognized and applauded. Whether she was young or older mattered very little. At one big cocktail party, the two belles were both women in their fifties, *soigneés élégantes*. They had

beaucoup de success—which, in the French phrase, meant success with the opposite sex. In fact, the value set on experience gave older women the edge.

A further clarification on the *beaucoup de success*. This does not mean that these women "picked up" men at this party. It simply means that men paid attention to these two older women and wanted to talk with them, paid them small courtesies and compliments. These women of a "certain age" were not ignored while the men focused time and attention only on younger women.

I have always wondered which was the cause and which the effect. Did women 40 and more in France put out effort to be attractive because the French culture is one that admires vintage in women as well as in wine? Or was it that in French culture, older women are appreciated because women over 40 maintain themselves in a manner to evoke appreciation?

One often reads that French men value older French women for their charm and experience. Charm and experience of mature women does not appear to be as greatly valued in the USA. Texas men are known to like their women "green." And we also know it is not only American men in Texas who often demonstrate a preference for young, immature, and inexperienced females.

Yet, for centuries, various French women have been remembered for charming and holding the affections of men decades younger than they. Diane de Poitiers comes to mind. The mistress of Henry II was 20 years older than the king. During the time Henry II was on the throne, Diane de Poitiers reigned as queen of France in all but title.

In *The Book of the Courtesans*, author Susan Griffin tells the story of French writer and courtesan Ninon de Lenclos aka Anne de Lanclos. She writes that when young Abbe Gedolyn began to pursue Ninon, she put him off for a while. But when she finally agreed to be his lover, she told the young man that he must wait for one month and one day to have her. He agreed. The day came. Susan Griffin writes:

> Happy in her arms at last, he asked her why she had made him wait exactly one month and a day. 'Because today is my birthday,' she answered, 'and I wanted to prove to myself that at the age of seventy, I am still capable of entertaining a lover.'

And just think! Ninon de Lenclos managed to remain capable without cosmetic surgery, hormone replacement therapy, or regular injections of Botox.

Actress Audrey Hepburn's second husband was nine years her junior. After her divorce from the Italian doctor, she found her soul mate and shared the last years of her life with actor Robert Wolders, seven years younger than she.

Even if in France and the rest of Europe, it is somewhat easier for a woman to remain desirable when she is in her fifties, sixties, and beyond, there are many, many women in the USA more than fifty who are doing quite nicely in this area, thank you. With more knowledge about nutrition and exercise, and with improvements in medicine, some of us past the half-century mark are more attractive and have more energy than when we were decades younger. I know that I certainly look better and feel better than when I was a severely overweight and acne-plagued teenager.

At the *Chic & Slim* website, I receive wonderful email from women telling me how, though they are in their fifties as I am, that they are having *beaucoup de success* with putting the

French-inspired *Chic & Slim* philosophy to work for them. I almost called this technique The Ooh-la-la Technique for reasons, if they are not yet obvious, soon will be. I received an email from a woman who had read the *Chic & Slim* books and was pleased with the results of her efforts toward a chic and elegant personal style. She wrote:

> Last week I was waiting for the elevator in the building where I work. I was wearing fitted wool trousers (with high heels, of course), a silk blouse and red lipstick. A co-worker, friend (male) came around the corner and, as God is my witness, stopped cold in his tracks and said, "Ooh-la-la!"

Certainly we are pleased when our physician praises our ability to keep our weight in the normal range. (One of the reasons I wrote the original *Chic & Slim* was the encouragement of my doctor who said I should tell others how I did it.) We are cheered when another woman of chic style compliments our appearance. But nothing gives us quite the satisfaction as a compliment or complimenting look from a male. Does not matter whether it be husband, lover, coworker, or a stranger who gives us an appreciative glance as he passes us on the street.

French women find great motivation for looking chic and staying slim in the approving looks, comments, and reactions of men. I have never been able to think of better motivation myself. Saying *"non, merci"* to piles of greasy pasta, drinking mineral water instead of sugared colas, roasting a chicken instead of bringing home a tub of KFC seems a small price to pay for those heartfelt *ooh-la-las*.

The Paris-born American fashion designer Pauline Trigere,

"an elegant symbol of American fashion for more than 50 years," was one of the most vocal advocates of using men for inspiration. In an article titled "Trigere created a design for living as well as for fashion," *Cleveland Plain Dealer* Fashion Editor Evelyn Theiss wrote :

> Fashion designer Pauline Trigere, who always looked about 20 years younger than her age, didn't mind sharing tips on how she achieved that: standing on her head, and having lovers.

Evelyn Theiss's article quotes Cleveland television personality and fitness guru Paige Palmer who knew the designer. She said that Pauline Trigere, "always maintained her posture, her looks and her weight. That's probably why she lived as long as she did." The designer died at age 93 and continued her business, entertaining, and active gardening almost to the end of her life.

Many might not want to take Pauline Trigere's advice too exactly. Instead of standing on our heads, we might achieve that daily reverse of blood flow with a slantboard. (Those of you who have visited the *Chic & Slim* website know that I am an enthusiastic user of a slantboard.) Instead of having lovers, we might find inspiration for our efforts to achieve attractive healthy bodies in the admiring looks and comments of men, including husbands.

A woman described by her interviewer for a *Town & Country* makeup article as "an elegant publishing consultant in Manhattan" said that "being in love is the number one beauty secret—it keeps you incandescent."

But let us give the last word on this topic to Diana Vreeland, who, as editor at *Harper's Bazaar* for 27 years and Editor-in-Chief at *Vogue* for ten years made a career out of advising women on fashion and lifestyle. In *Young At Any Age: thirty-three of the world's most elegant women reveal how they stay beautiful*, Diana Vreeland declares emphatically: "It's impossible for a woman to look really good without a man."

But what if a woman does not have a man in her life, the interviewer asked? To this, Diana Vreeland responded: "If you can't find one, make him up." Invent a man, look really good for him, and a real man will come along, she promises.

How You Do It For Chic & Slim Success:

⤳ When tempted to skip some part of your grooming routine such as your regular shampoo and watch a television show instead, picture in your mind a man whose good opinion you value turning away from you to watch an attractive woman with shiny, clean hair walk down the street.

⤳ When tempted to eat food for which your body has no need, picture in your mind the man of your dreams. Ask yourself which you would prefer, the taste of that chocolate bar or spending some time with him.

⤳ Write a description of the kind of man with whom you would like to have a relationship, find a photo in a magazine or newspaper that shows his style. Then, design a personal style and a lifestyle to please him.

Supporting Information for *Chic & Slim* Books

Chic & Slim *le website*

a n n e b a r o n e . c o m

chic & slim Email to Anne

Dear Anne,

I'm a very contented newcomer to your site! Your books, your philosophy, your spirit....have all come into my life at just the perfect time! Just when I'm facing all those transformations that happen around that "certain age", your wealth of new ideas for thinking and living have made me feel as though I'm a teenager again....on the threshold of something very exciting!! In just one week everything about my life seems new and fresh again! I've had an utterly decadent and self indulgent time reading your books and web articles (while sipping tea and taking tiny nibbles of "LU" cookies, of course!) as well as many other materials you've recommended (while sipping tea and taking tiny nibbles of "LU" cookies, of course!).

Every so often I jump up and make some major change in my environment, wardrobe, etc! It's as if I am now looking at everything with new eyes. It is SO GREAT! Oh, and (I almost forgot!)....the morning after ! the day I received and devoured your first book I got up and made French Bread from scratch. I used to enjoy doing that years ago when my kids were little...I even grind the wheat fresh. Your recipes are fantastic!

Anyway, who should "coincidentally" show up just as the bread came out but our friend (male) from France! We ended up doing a whole French day with the midday meal lasting all day! He was astounded to see my enthusiasm (and questions for him) for anything French! He has dropped by many more times this week and I've sent him home with baked goodies. He said he's never before seen such enthusiasm for the French since he's been in this country!

Anne, I could go on and on with praise and thanks to you! So many wonderful things are happening as a result of your books. Thank you so very much for your extraordinary efforts. And keep those website articles coming...I so look forward to them and enjoy hearing about what you're doing!

Sincerely,

Janna in Malibu

chic & slim Technique 3
CHIC ANYWHERE

Wherever they are, French women arrange themselves in that hard-to-define, but you-know-it-when-you-see-it French chic. No matter what their activity, French women always manage to look alluring and attractive in that special French way. Chic French women are invariably slim. Or, they dress cleverly enough that you think they are slim.

Women in the USA today look to comfort in clothes. Comfort can translate into sloppy and unflattering outfits worn so loose that women have room to overeat without discomfort and easily gain weight. "Sensible" shoes make women look (and feel) frumpy and unfeminine.

This technique is designed to guide you in developing a workable chic that makes you appear attractive and helps you stay slim *n'importe où*, no matter where you live or travel.

～

The N'Importe Où Technique
THE CHIC & SLIM ANYWHERE TECHNIQUE

T he email and letters communicate the worry. Women worry that developing a chic personal style à la française means you must adopt a body-clinging and stiletto-heeled Parisienne chic. The writers say, "Parisienne chic won't work for my lifestyle where I live." Most often, they are right.

Smart little suits with skin-tight skirts worn with stiletto heels if you trying to keep up with active toddlers on the playground are not very practical for Mississippi in August. Nor for heading out to work in the morning in Michigan during three weeks of blizzard in January. One thing that Parisienne women have aiding their chic is that the weather never varies greatly in Paris. The extremes of heat and cold found in many regions of the world are not a problem in the French capital.

Never fear. French chic is much more than Parisienne chic. French women, depending on where they find themselves, play different variations on the theme of French chic. They can achieve Riviera beach chic or French countryside chic as well as Parisienne chic.

Stanley Marcus, long a guiding light of *Neiman Marcus* stores, understood that not only American women in New York had an interest in quality design in fashion. As *Washington Post* Staff Writer Robin Givhan wrote in a tribute to the legendary retailer at the time of his death in 2002, "Marcus knew that elegance was not tied to geography." He understood this concept so well that back in 1953, Vogue magazine called Dallas's *Neiman Marcus* "Texas with a French accent."

What Stanley Marcus also understood was that women, depending on the region in which they lived, would achieve their chic in different ways. As Robin Givhan explains in the above-mentioned article: "Marcus believed in elegance, equating it with a keen understanding of appropriateness. And in that definition, he tapped into a critical difference between a New York fashion sense and the rest of the country."

Chic must be appropriate to the place in which you live.

In another *Washington Post* fashion article, Lars Nilsson, the new designer for Bill Blass is quoted. "We may do a trunk show in Portland, Oregon, and then in Palm Beach, and people are not going to buy the same things because the climate is so different," he says.

That is the reason that the company has recently developed an all silk flannel in place of the usual wool or cashmere flannel. ". . . because people in Palm Beach can wear gray flannel pants and not be too hot."

You can use Paris for inspiration, then design your own appropriate personal style for wherever you live — as did this woman did who recently visited Paris. After she returned to the USA, she emailed:

> I visited Paris recently with a friend. Our last evening there, we went to the Opera Garnier and saw a modern ballet. During the intermission we went to the Grand Salon and watched people. I've never seen so many terrific-looking older ladies in my life! It was quite an inspiration to me. Their style was in line with what you mentioned in *Encore* -

Simple chin-length haircuts. Natural-looking
makeup. Very nice pant-suits in neutral colors.
Small gold earrings. And that's about it. Of
course, they were all very slim. Now, thanks to
you, I know how they do it.

No matter where you live, you should be able to purchase
a tailored pant suit in a neutral black, gray, brown, or navy, as
well as, some small gold earrings and a decent pair of leather
pumps in a color to match your pant suit. Instructions for
applying the kind of natural looking makeup French women
prefer is there in makeup artist Bobbi Brown's book *Bobbi
Brown Beauty*. As for the chic Parisienne hairstyle, I wear a
simple chin-length bob. The town to which I drive, where my
hairdresser Bev does that haircut, has a population of 2800. A
good hairdresser is not defined by geography, but by his or
her individual talent and willingness to stay current on styles
and cutting techniques.

Wherever French women are, they are always observing
other women, looking for good ideas for their own stylish
dressing from the informal fashion shows passing by. It is
wonderful when, like the woman in the previous email and
her friend, you can hang out at the *Opéra Garnier* or a little
Parisian sidewalk cafe and watch chic French women. But what
about those who do not have time or money to travel to Paris
or New York? Where do you get your inspiration for your
personal style when so many women you see out and around
in the USA are such poor role models for chic?

Fashion magazines, once a wonderful source of inspiration,
have, for the most part, become useless as a resource for a
good many of us. Unless you are 18-years-old, at least six-feet-
one inches tall and are well on your way to anorexia, the photos
don't give much idea of what the clothes would actually look

like on you. Many fashion photos lately are so arty that you can't really tell how the clothes would look even on the 18-year-old, giraffe-tall anorexics. Prices on the fashions shown are prohibitive for many of us, even for those of us who make quality investment purchases. A lot of us just don't have budgets that allow $2200 casual jackets to wear with $900 *torn* Gucci jeans and $1300 purses.

Television and websites often provide much better opportunities than fashion magazines to see what designs you will find influencing what is for sale. Many television shows are very fashion conscious. Some of the series are watched as much for their fashions as for the plot. (Sometimes the fashions are far better than the plot.) Flicking the remote control almost any time of day will give you a variety of current styles. Also, the women on TV offer models in a wider range of ages and sizes than mostly young, mostly ultra thin, abnormally tall fashion models who are usually camera-angled and PhotoShop re-imaged into even greater perfection than God, their dermatologist, their orthodontist, and their cosmetic surgeon has rendered them.

Even if you don't speak a word of Spanish, tune into the Spanish language stations. You will see some extremely well-dressed women. The thing I particularly like on Spanish language television is these women have thighs. Seeing these attractive women gives hope to those of us, who, even when our weight is in the normal range, find that our genetic and ethnic makeup dictates that we have meat between our knees and hipbone.

On the website *Style.com* you can click on the name of most major designers and see a slide show of what most recently came down their runway, just as if you had attended the shows. You even get back views in many images. Most designers have websites from which you can order the styles that strike your fancy. And, of course, there are all those catalogs that can be ordered for free or a small price.

If your budget is limited, survey the styles on TV and the Internet and in catalogs for a general idea of what you wish to buy. Then, go to the good stores and examine carefully quality items beyond your budget to see how they are designed and made. Next go to a store (or another department in that store) that is within your budget and see how close you can come to finding that style and quality in an item you can afford.

A fact of life here that French women accept: Shopping for the right chic clothes requires an investment of time and effort. And you must keep a firm grip on fashion magazine editor Diana Vreeland's dictum: Elegance is refusal. You are going to spend a lot more time *not* buying items you find than you are going to spend finding what you require.

FBI operatives could learn things from watching a French woman setting off in search of just the right piece to add to her wardrobe. This is not a fun day out. This is serious business. And if you reach for the same garment on the rack at the same time as a French women in serious shopping mode, if you are smart, you will let her have it. Trust me on this.

With many major ready-to-wear lines offering catalog or website ordering, you need no longer make trips to major cities to find chic style. Though in my mother's generation, a shopping trip to Dallas 125 miles away with a stay in a hotel and lunch in those places that catered to the "ladies who lunch" could be a nice little holiday. My aunt reminisced recently that on those shopping trips you, of course, wore high-heeled shoes, hat and gloves to shop, especially for *Neiman Marcus*. Today for my "shopping trips," I can sit at my bedroom iMac in my nightgown, barefoot, sipping hot tea. I mouse-click my way through the season's collections.

You do you not need to copy Paris or New York for your

own personal style. The *Chic & Slim* books are designed to give you the basic underlying principles of French chic. You can then translate those principles to your own lifestyle — as I did for my lifestyle on the Texas Riviera and now in North Texas.

By the way, speaking for various women's groups here in Wichita Falls, Texas, this past year, I found quite a number of women who put together their own personal brand of chic that would look at home on the streets of Paris, yet are extremely practical for their North Texas lifestyle. Some of these women travel often to France. But even those who do not travel to France find inspiration and the clothes for great personal style.

I was particularly happy to receive an email some months ago from another Texas woman who related how she was adapting *Chic & Slim* to her own lifestyle.

> When you described your reasons for living where you do, I was a little perplexed as to how I could have a Chic & Slim lifestyle. My husband and I have moved to rural East Texas and are building a log home. The local Wal-Mart and Brookshire's do not have very good produce or bread. I'm not sure about walking on the roads — we are REALLY in the sticks! {sigh} But I thought about it and decided to think like a Frenchwoman living in the countryside. I do know where to get wonderful homemade tortillas and I do go to the city of Tyler some and there is a great French bakery there. When we finish our home I want to put in walking trails - we are on 40 acres so there is plenty of space. Also, I like to cook and plan to learn to make bread. During much of the year there are road side veggie stands.

As any French woman would, this woman in East Texas is focusing on what she has available, not on what is unavailable. French women take a positive attitude toward their personal style and lifestyle. They don't spend much time on the negatives or on what they can't find or can't afford. They work out clever solutions. They don't look for excuses.

With some wonderful exceptions, however, most of us live in locales where, if we are going to have good bread at reasonable prices, we are going to have to bake it ourselves. Thankfully, you can now buy great bread machines for around $50. Using a bread machine or food processor to knead the bread dough takes most of the work out of the process. Fortunately, excellent flours are available in the United States. Many of us will have to drive to another city or order those flours, but the nutritional and taste benefits are worth it, I believe.

Likewise, in many regions of the USA, it takes time to locate what you need for a *Chic & Slim* lifestyle. *Chic & Slim* appeals to a rather exclusive group of individuals. What is needed for this lifestyle are not the foods and services most people in the area demand. Slowly, I am locating many of the food items and services that I thought were unavailable here in barbecue and blue jeans North Texas. Some of my recent finds are the brand of free-range eggs (though as I was doing final corrections on this book, I learned that store is closing), good goat cheese, croissants and brioche (reasonable facsimiles for real French items), and tofu made from certified non-genetically modified soybeans. In the meantime, the situation with fresh produce has improved from dismal to not-too-bad. Most of the time I can even find reasonably decent lettuces. I might want Romaine and have to settle for red leaf, but usually I can find some lettuce fresh enough to be edible, even if the price is about double what I paid in South Texas.

You will have better success developing a *Chic & Slim* lifestyle no matter where you live if you focus on what is available and how you can use what is available to make your personal style the best possible for you. All it takes is a little French-style daring and confidence in your own ability to make the right style choices for you.

How You Do It For Chic & Slim Success:

✂ In designing your own chic personal style, consider climate and local standards and taboos.

✂ Make a list of the activities for which you must regularly be dressed appropriately and make sure your personal style will be adequate to them.

✂ In the interest of efficient use of time, note what activities you must perform without stopping to change clothes. Make sure your wardrobe includes clothes that can make this transition.

✂ Look for style examples on television and on *style.com*.

✂ Determine what styles look good on you — not on someone else.

✂ Check out the expensive shops to see how quality is designed and constructed. If your budget is limited, try to find the closest approximation in lower priced clothes.

✂ Locate a good resale shop for quality clothes.

✂ Be daring and confident in designing your chic personal style.

✂ Consider locating good produce, cheeses, and other requirements for your *Chic & Slim* lifestyle as an interesting challenge. Hone your detective skills and see what you can find.

✂ Use the great search features of *www.google.com* to locate food items not available locally that are sold on the Internet.

Your Personal Style melds your lifestyle, finances, and identity into an overall fashion statement that makes you feel good about yourself and tells the world how to feel about you. . . . Getting the looks part out of the way allows you to get down to business and the true priorities of your life.

Suzy Gershman
Best Dressed

The process of growth, of being an independent person, of learning who you are and what you want from life, is the real secret of life, happiness, and beauty. . . . A fulfilled woman is a beautiful woman.

Diane von Furstenberg
Diane von Furstenberg's Book of Beauty

chic & slim Technique 6
MUSIQUE

French women maintain an aura of confident serenity. They eat carefully and slowly. They have energy to conduct their active, busy, and well-ordered lives.

American women are often so rushed in their daily lives that they gobble their food. The pace of their lives renders them too exhausted to exercise. They eat excess calories to give themselves quick energy. They often appear (and feel) harassed.

This technique will help you use certain kinds of music to soothe and heal you so that you will be more serene, help you slow your eating so that you chew carefully and slowly so that you digest your food more properly. You will be slimmer and have more energy for your lifestyle.

The Mystique Technique
THE AURA OF MYSTERY TECHNIQUE

Mystique. What a delicious French word!

Their mystique, their aura of mystery, ranks as one of the key reasons men find French women so attractive and desirable. But what exactly is mystique? How does having mystique aid French women in developing and maintaining successful and satisfying romantic relationships? How does it aid their relationships with all who know them? More importantly, how can you develop your mystique to enhance your attractiveness and make your relationships more successful and satisfying?

In discussing mystique, it is sometimes easier to describe a woman lacking mystique than to describe one who possesses it.

An example of a woman lacking mystique was an overweight, tightly-permanented woman seated near me on a commuter flight. In the 42 minutes between boarding and landing, she bombarded her seat mate and (most of the rest of the plane since she had a loud, projecting voice) with the story of her life. By the time the plane's wheels touched down on the destination tarmac, we all knew how she met her husband, the problems of her marriage, the saga of her divorce, where she worked, her mother's health, her dog's cute tricks. We were even treated to a brief description of her summer's vacation.

As we escaped into the airport terminal, there was nothing more any of us wanted to know about that woman. Mystique rating: 0.

Women in the USA in recent decades have not been known for possessing mystique. Though there was a character in a Henry James novel about whom he wrote something to the effect that she was rumored to have shot a man somewhere in Oregon. Not that she had given interviews to Connie Chung, CNN, and Hard Copy about the reasons for shooting someone in Oregon, followed immediately by soundbites of interviews with the victim's friends and family. No, it was just that there was some suggestion, quiet whispers . . . no one knew for sure . . . but she might have shot someone, sometime previously, possibly in Oregon. But then it could have been in California. . . . Ah, the mystery. Wouldn't it be interesting if sometime in conversation with her, she might give us hints as to what really happened? That woman had definite mystique.

Women who talk incessantly about themselves squelch any mystique they might have. We know all. Too soon.

A critique of American women's mystique-stifling talk about themselves came in a song by country music star Toby Keith. In his song that hit the top of the Billboard charts in late 2001, Toby Keith complains not just that women talk so incessantly about themselves, but he catalogs the specific topics that he would just as soon not hear about.

As someone who writes about French women, I was interested to find that the specific topics Toby Keith complains about in his song are those that French women would likely not mention in conversation with a man: skin care, wardrobe problems, gynecological topics.

When someone knows the process, the how-it-was-accomplished, the aura of mystery is gone. French women likely would not mention most of the topics on Toby Keith's list because they would see such information as detrimental to their mystique. They do not want too many facts about family, former lovers, work situations to spoil their aura of mystery. They want men to be entranced by the results of their personal style efforts, not discuss the process with them. Besides, French women design their workable personal style and lifestyle to prevent health and wardrobe problems from occurring.

Owen Edwards, writing in an article on makeup in *Town & Country* magazine, said: "I have yet to observe my European wife putting on more than lipstick. I know that something happens in her Continental privacy, but she feels no need to let me see what it is."

And she certainly doesn't talk about it, I will bet.

The French enthusiastically discuss films, books, politics, social problems, the current political scandal. They always seem to have a scandal to discuss. But French men and women seem to have more interesting things to talk about than those mundane matters that inspired Toby Keith's song.

Sometime around the early 1970s, I noticed that many American women began to define being liberated as the right to use profanity and discuss their menstrual problems in mixed company. Sometime around the early 1990s, I noticed many women talking about their problems with menopause. Really, ladies, there are more interesting topics. Especially when people are eating.

In a *Washington Post* article in January 2002, Staff Writer Paul Farhi, writing about Toby Keith's song "I Wanna Talk About Me," quotes radio personality Don Geronimo: "Look, my wife is wonderful. But when I ask her a question, it would be nice if she could condense the answer. All I want is the first and last paragraph, and not all the details in between. That, in essence, is what I pray for in my life."

Women wanting to develop a mystique as entrancing as a French woman's would do well to take Don Geronimo's request as a guideline. The first paragraph and the last, especially on a topic that holds little interest to men. (And don't send me letters and email about equality. We aren't talking about equality here. We are talking about how to have a workable relationship with a man on the French model.)

Two things help your mystique: first spend less time talking, especially on topics for which your listener likely has no interest. Second, become a better listener. This advice applies to conversations with everyone, not just someone with whom you have or want a relationship.

Women would also do well to take a lesson from French women to become better and more sympathetic listeners. Again, and again, I note when someone writes about an interesting and intriguing woman there is a comment or quote about what a good listener she was. Jacqueline Kennedy Onassis, one American woman whose mystique was often noted, was known for focusing completely on a companion in conversation and listening intently. But, you say, so many people are so boring. How can you be expected to give complete attention to a bore who is prattling on about something for which you have no interest?

Again take a lesson from Jackie. She was reported to be adroit at gracefully escaping people who might bore her. One article writer (I have forgotten which) wrote of approaching Jackie and giving his name and saying that (a mutual acquaintance) had suggested he introduce himself to her. 'Oh, and I am so glad you did," Jackie said warmly. And then turned and walked away.

You can always just say "Excuse me," politely, give no other explanation, and walk away. How do they know whether you are rushing to an important business meeting, or desperately needing a bathroom because of medication you are taking? French women's aloofness is also useful when it comes to avoiding bores. Life is short. Spend your listening time on interesting people. Avoid the rest. And have no guilt about not wasting the precious minutes of your life listening to people who talk too much about themselves. If you avoid them, perhaps that will be a good lesson to them that they should find something more interesting to talk about than themselves.

American women are known to complain that men cause problems in a relationship because they are hesitant to express their feelings. From the perspective of my certain age, I think that often when American women complain that American men do not express their feelings, many times they are really complaining that men do not express the feelings for them that these women want men to say they feel. He may not be telling you that he loves you passionately, because he may not. He may just be tolerating you. He may be thinking: This woman keeps nagging me about expressing my feelings, and I'm out of here. You have to earn adoration. And few women have earned adoration complaining about unexpressed feelings.

In any case, women have extraordinary capacity to read the feelings and nonverbal communication of infants and toddlers. Savvy women apply the same techniques to reading the nonverbal communication of men. You may have to read from actions what men cannot say in words. And you may be glad you did. A man's actions may often times be more eloquent than his words. I remember a dinner in which I served a particularly delicious veal scaloppini. I observed one of the male guests eating the dish with much pleasure and gusto. He was a man for whom words did not come easily, but under the inspiration of the moment, he beamed down at his plate and commented, "This stuff is really good. It's not a bit greasy."

If French men are more likely than American men to speak

words that thrill a woman, it may be that French women have put much effort into inspiring those feelings. It may be too that the Gallic personality is more inclined than the Anglo-Saxon to expressing passionate feelings in poetic words. And it may be that a Frenchman has had much practice saying the *same* poetic words to a lot of *different* women —sometimes several different women in the same week.

You can always hear better when you listen quietly. French women's serenity that is so often praised is frequently conducted in silence. French women are not chatty for the most part. They can be brilliant conversationalists, but they don't generally chatter. They can sit quietly and contentedly. And many men just want some freedom from verbal input, especially at home. There is value in learning to perfect a quiet tranquility, one in which you are silent, not because you are angry and upset, but silent because you are content.

Given this whole situation of male-female conversation, might it not make sense to choose to have a relationship with someone who talks about things in which you are interested. And might it not also be wise to broaden yourself and take an interest in what your husband and/or lover are interested in?

In a 1986 *Vogue* article, "Anouk Aimee: The Female Mystique," Joan Juliet Buck wrote:

> She does not want to give anything away about herself. This doesn't stop her from being friendly, funny, straightforward, touching, full of hope and good sense. . .But ask her a personal question. . .and she looks the other way, giggles, and says, "I hate interviews."

Joan Buck goes on to write; "To spend time with her is to learn a little about the quiet, receptive way to be a woman."

I think the word *receptive* should be noted, particularly in the context of men's willingness or unwillingness to share feelings. Might it be possible, that if a woman is talking so much about herself, she does not appear to be receptive to information from another? Also I think both men and women are hesitant to share personal feelings with someone who is a "talker." Because you worry that person would share your personal information with too many others.

Town & Country magazine's Special Issue January 2002 "All The Best" featured Catherine Deneuve on the cover. What better poster girl for *the best*? In an article in that issue, film critic Andrew Sarris describes the French actress as "an imperishable icon of all that bespeaks beauty and elegance in French civilization." He quotes from Ephraim Katz's *Film Encyclopedia* entry that described Catherine Deneuve as an "exquisite, fragile beauty, aloof and detached in manner." He says: "I have remained entranced by the mysteries suggested by her marvelously sculpted features, her ever-inquiring eyes, her svelte, often enchantingly attired figure, her modestly revealed charms, which promise so much while exposing so little." He says the actress has retained a core of seriousness that "intoxicates even as it mystifies."

What two better examples of French mystique than these two French actresses Anouk Aimee and Catherine Deneuve, women of a "certain age," yet still alluring and desirable and entrancing men?

The easy thing about developing mystique is that others will do much of the work for you. They will — if you let them. If you don't talk much about yourself, other people will start making things up.

Often, as I related in *Chic & Slim Encore*, other people can make up far more glamourous stories about you than is actual fact.

And of course, you neither directly confirm nor deny those stories. That would spoil your mystique.

Developing or perfecting mystique will make you more attractive and desirable — whatever your age.

How You Do It For Chic & Slim Success:

➤ Talk less about yourself.

➤ In casual conversation, avoid sharing personal information more appropriate to conversation with your gynecologist, your hairdresser, your aesthetician, or the clerk at a dress boutique.

➤ Practice listening. Look at the person to whom you are listening. Focus on what they are telling you.

➤ Develop the capacity for quiet tranquility.

➤ To escape bores, say "Excuse me" politely and walk away.

➤ Avoid people who annoy or depress you.

➤ Read or watch at least three media articles a day, read at least one book every few weeks, take an interest in the activities of your community, nation, and world so that you have other topics of conversation besides yourself.

➤ Become knowledgeable on some subject you would be unlikely to know about and bring it up in conversation. If you live in Manhattan, it might be mountain goats. If you live on a farm in Iowa, it might be cactus. People will be intrigued.

You don't have to wear an amazing dress to be stunning—simplicity is sometimes more lovely. A beautiful personality shines through clothes.

Opera singer Angela Gheorghiu
on Style in *Woman's Journal*

chic & slim Email to Anne
MEMORIES OF A CHIC FRENCH WOMAN

Hello Anne,

I found your site quite by accident by searching for "making picante sauce" on *Google.com*. I was immediately reminded of a French lady that I worked for during my teen years. I was always amazed at the things that she ate and yet stayed so skinny. She would fix lunch for the both of us and eat as much as I did. Keep in mind that I was a 6'1", 190 pound, high school football player and she was a very petite lady in her late 70's! She would buy the fattest cheeses and bake the most wonderful breads. Then she would make homemade salad dressings and homemade mayonnaise. She would carve roast beef or roast leg-of-lamb and make the best sandwiches I ever had. We would also eat a simple salad and some fresh fruit. I was a teetotaler, but she would drink a little wine with every meal.

She lived alone with two dogs and a parakeet, but she always surrounded herself with beautiful things. She had a lot of art and also painted some herself.

My job was to help her with yard work. She didn't have a yard, but a series of huge flower beds. She also had a small greenhouse and I took care of orchids in it for her.

She would spend (what seemed like) hours every morning pampering herself and then join me in my gardening tasks for an hour or so before going back inside to prepare our meal. Meal preparation took another hour or so even if it was a sandwich. In the evenings, she would paint, entertain friends, or drive to the farmer's market. When any of her friends flew anywhere she would insist they bring her back some fresh fruit. I have eaten fresh bananas that were shaped like baseballs and fresh kiwis that are nothing like the ones you buy in a store.

I never got to eat at a restaurant with her, but she told me that she would never eat out anywhere that did not serve on china plates with silverware. Of course I took that to mean that she never ate fast food.

I think she took a lot of time to enjoy life and the simple pleasures around her. She never got in a hurry about anything. When she was going out to town, she would have me wash her car (a little Mercedes) and warm the engine about 15 minutes before she left.

She lived (and I still live) in the mountains near Asheville, NC. The pace of life here is very slow and people enjoy things (like neighbors) here more than any other place I've been.

I appreciate your web site and reading some of it brings back vivid memories of this lady who enjoyed life.

Patrick in North Carolina

Anne Barone Comments:

Patrick's memories paint a wonderful portrait of a chic French woman. If you have read my previous *Chic & Slim* books, recall the factors in French slimness that I described. Observe how this woman's lifestyle shows these factors in practice. She is motivated to devote special attention to her appearance. She takes exercise from her daily activities, in this case gardening. Also note that she has no lawn, just flower beds. Meals she serves are simple, but high quality food is carefully prepared and eaten leisurely and with pleasure. Quality possessions, such as her car, are well cared for.

Best of all, this woman lived her chic French lifestyle in a rural area of the USA. She shows us that you can live chic and slim *à la française* no matter where you reside. Patrick's portrait of this chic French woman provides us with a wonderful role model.

chic & slim Email to Anne

Hello Anne,

I just wanted to thank you for your website and your postings. I read them daily and always find them thought provoking as well as entertaining. These days, reading them provides a pleasant sense of civilization which you so inspire. I also love your sense of humor. Thanks again, Anne.

Cynthia in Naples, Florida

Bonjour Madame Barone,

I have greatly enjoyed both books—the first one I read in several hours the first night I got it ! I have also scoured your website and find it both informative and enjoyable! Thank you for making this available. I have been trying to find a "fit" for myself — somewhere between Birkenstock-wearing simplicity seekers (simplicity, yes, but no Birkies!) and the all out, jumbo-size-it consumer society in which we live. You make it seem easy !

Elizabeth in Atlanta

Dear Anne,

Can't tell you how much continuing help I get from keeping your book at work and reading it as I enjoy lunch. Keeps me focused on higher thoughts, rather than mindless partaking calories. Thanks, as always, for your contribution to the lives of chic n' slim women everywhere!

Karen Noske

chic & slim Technique 5
ÉLÉGANCE

The French rarely snack. Most of the food they consume is eaten at meals. When the French do eat between their three regular daily meals, the snack is generally enjoyed seated, eaten from a plate with eating utensils. (The French aren't much into eaten-from-the-hand foods.) Avoidance of mindless eating of high-calorie foods between meals is a chief factor in French slimness.

Americans snack frequently. High-calorie, low-nutrition, eaten-from -the-hand foods are available in practically every neighborhood 24 hours-a-day, seven days a week. Snacking in the USA on high calorie, low nutrition foods consumed when the attention is often elsewhere is a major cause of the obesity epidemic in the USA.

This technique is designed to aid you in cutting out the mindless eating between meals that is adding excess high-calorie low-nutrition food to your daily intake and contributing to excess weight and other health problems.

>m~

The Élégance Technique
THE NO SNACKING TECHNIQUE

I n a scene in the 1990 French film May Fools directed by Louis Malle, the character played by actress Miou-Miou wanders around the kitchen mindlessly gnawing a carrot stick as she prepares a meal. The third time I saw this movie I realized this carrot chewing was to demonstrate that the character had a problem with food. This between-meal snacking contributed to her excess weight (about 5 pounds as far as I could see, but you know how the French feel about five pounds).

In the USA, eating raw carrot sticks between meals is often a suggested activity for weight reduction. The French consider eating carrot sticks between meals, especially while standing, as contributing to a weight problem.

Americans are the world's champion snackers. And they have the obesity statistics to prove it. Government figures now classify more than 120 million Americans as either overweight or obese. In their *Washington Post* article, "Supersize Country," Shannon Brownlee, a Markle Senior Fellow at the New America Foundation, and Patti Wolter , a senior editor at *Self* magazine wrote:

> The larger problem lies with the environment. We are surrounded by tasty, cheap, high-fat food, while fruits and vegetables are comparatively more expensive and less readily

available. Our suburbs are built without sidewalks, our kids buy candy and soda in the hallways at school, and our sense of portion size is so out of control that we think a 600-calorie cinnamon bun (about a quarter of the total calories the average man needs per day) is a snack. We could not have designed an environment more conducive to getting fat.

Americans reportedly spend $30 billion a year on snacks. What is interesting to me about this figure is that $30 billion is also the figure usually given for the amount spent on weight control products in the USA. According to an article by Sandra Gordon, the European Snack Food Association reported that 81 percent of the French surveyed expressed a belief that eating between meals could be a problem or was unhealthy.

Another interesting statistic from Sandra Gordon was that from numerous studies conducted by David Levitsky, professor of nutritional sciences at Cornell, he found that when people snack, they often eat as much at their next meal as if they had not snacked.

I discovered from personal experience that when I snacked between meals, I often wanted *more* food at meals than if I had not snacked. One explanation for this was that I often snacked on highly sugared carbohydrate foods such as cookies. This sugar set off carbohydrate cravings.

I call this technique designed to help you give up snacking The Elégance Technique because, for decades, it has been my suspicion that a chief reason French women don't snack between meals is they don't want to run the risk of messing up their lipstick and their clothes. Especially their clothes. Those small wardrobes of quality clothes do not have many spares in case of accident.

This suspicion received support when I read an article by Barbara Bradley, Fashion Editor for the Memphis newspaper *The Commercial Appeal* . The article compared the way women dressed in the USA and Europe. The article quotes Claire Dupuis, manager of apparel fashion marketing for Cotton Incorporated, who notes the confidence European women demonstrate in their style, how they appreciate the details of well constructed clothes, how they pay careful attention to the fit, and how they prefer to maintain a wardrobe of a small number of well chosen "investment clothes" to buying many less expensive garments the way American women do.

Barbara Bradley writes: "Okay, but say you're circling the burger palace with fries balanced on your dashboard, and splat! Your $2,000 designer suit suddenly acquires a new Heinz logo. Didn't your investment just tank?"

The response from Claire Dupuis (no mention that she is French, but the name is certainly French) is that most Europeans do not balance fries on their dashboards, nor do they juggle food in their hands as they walk down a street. "They sit down to lunch and eat in a civilized manner," she reminds us.

See what I mean about elegance? You are less likely to smear your mouth or spill food on your clothes if you are eating seated at the table with a napkin in your lap. In situations that permit it, the French are also likely to tie a huge table napkin around their neck to further protect their clothes. Watch those chic French women eat and they practically dive over their plates when they take a bite. Any falling crumbs will tumble directly into the plate. If you want to see a demonstration of this, see the scene in the film *Un Coeur en Hiver (A Heart in Winter)* where the actress Emmanuelle Béart is eating a piece of cheese (The cheese is to revive her, she is claiming to feel weak). She bends her head low over the plate as she takes the tiniest nibble of cheese. While you are watching this, note that this is about as close as you are going to come to a French snack and that the character eats seated with her attention on her cheese. It is clear in the film's context that this nibble of cheese is not something she would do normally, but simply because she is feeling weak and needs some strength-giving fat and protein.

Snacking can also have its perils. As I was writing this book, we had an extreme example of the perils of mindless eating when President George W. Bush, eating a pretzel while watching a sports event on television, reportedly fainted and fell to the floor. Especially for a woman, falling off your chair unconscious with a pretzel in your mouth is not very elegant.

The benefit to giving up snacking is that you will be less likely to do something that will make you appear inelegant. You will be less likely to soil or ruin your chic, well-chosen clothes. You are going to have enough problems keeping the food spills off your lapel when you are concentrating on your food seated at a table.

So how do you make the transition from someone who eats frequently between meals to someone who, as the French do, generally eats only at regular meals or at a seated snack such as afternoon tea? (Remember that I do not consider afternoon tea a snack. Afternoon tea is sanity-saving therapy.)

If you have been snacking between meals, you have your digestive system programmed to respond with the appropriate digestive juices at those times. When you don't eat at that time you have been snacking, at first you will experience discomfort, a "mind hunger" —though it most likely will not be true hunger if you have eaten a proper meal.

You will have more success giving up snacks if you do so gradually one snack time at a time. One reason diets don't work is that diets require you to give up ALL those high calorie snacks you have been stuffing in to gratify every whim of advertising-induced and habit-induced hunger at all hours of the day and night, and substitute something totally unsatisfying. Every morning you have been eating this lovely Danish pastry from this wonderful little bakery with your 10:00 AM *cafe latte*, and now you are supposed to substitute a cheddar rice cake spread with a tablespoon of low fat cottage cheese and a cup of herbal tea. Oh goody, goody! Yuck!

If you are in the habit of eating a bowl of ice cream or <shudder> cereal before bedtime, work on giving up this snack first. Especially the cereal. Remember, cereal is not chic!

If you can delay your dinner until 7:30 or 8:00 PM, as the French do, this will help. Especially when I have eaten my evening meal between 6:00 and 7:00 PM, I find that I often become hungry again if I stay up much beyond 10 PM. So if just-before-bedtime snacking is a problem for you, you may have to eat your evening meal later, or go to bed a bit earlier. Or both.

When I am getting up around 5:00 AM, I find that I cannot work as productively in that stretch from before dawn until noon unless I eat breakfasts in two shifts. Then when I begin sleeping later, I find that I have to give up that second session of breakfast before it begins to add pounds. If I find myself getting hungry mid morning, scheduling shopping or other errands during this time makes tolerating the discomfort until my body readjusts to the lack of food between breakfast and lunch easier. If I was sitting at the word processor trying to write, the hunger discomfort would distract me and make it difficult for me to concentrate. Usually it only takes three or four days, or at most a week, to get through the worst part of the craving at that time.

If you are thinking of doing an at-home spa weekend, soaking in a luxuriating mineral salt or bubble bath is a good way to get through the snack craving until your digestive system adjusts to no food at this time. Please, please don't tell me you normally snack while soaking in the tub.

A technique that I used for combating a specific snack craving was self-hypnosis tapes. I do not like real ice cream any more (too sweet, too cold), but for some reason, several years ago I developed a passion for a specific soft frozen dessert cone sold at Hardee's. There was a Hardee's on the street I always took for shopping, and I reached a point that I could not pass Hardee's any afternoon without stopping for a cone. I found I was thinking up reasons to go shopping so I could stop for a cone. I realized that I must stop the cones before they began to show up on my hips and tummy.

Several years ago subliminal persuasion and self-hypnosis and guided imagery tapes were very popular. You could buy them in any book store. Pop one in your cassette tape player, sit or lie down in quiet place where you were unlikely to be disturbed, and listen to the words and music on the tape. Different tapes were designed to help you lose weight, cure insomnia, improve your performance in sports, stop smoking, achieve financial success, and deal with stress.

I cured a decades-old problem with insomnia using a subliminal persuasion/self-hypnosis tape that I bought on a whim in the bookstore one day. Later I happened to find (I think I was sitting in a dentist's waiting room) a magazine how-to article in *Reader's Digest* about scripting your own self-hypnosis tape. I decided to create a tape to help me give up my soft dessert cone snack habit.

Using a weight control self-hypnosis tape whose format I liked as a model, I scripted my own tape to deal with my desert cone obsession and several other habits that I thought it best that I discontinue. I recorded this tape speaking my text into a cassette recorder.

Self-hypnosis tapes are effective when played as you are falling asleep because research has shown that your subconscious can absorb information even when you sleep. It is useful to put the information into your conscious too. I also listened to the tape as I walked for exercise. After about six weeks use, I found myself no longer craving the cones. That was more than 10 years ago, and I only remember eating a soft frozen dessert once since. (Though I did eat a couple of bites from a similar type of frozen dessert that my son purchased at a Wendy's.) I think about buying one of those cones from time to time when I am somewhere they are sold. But somehow I never do. Something internal seems to stop me.

The Cure Insomnia self-hypnosis/subliminal persuasion tape that I found helpful was one written and recorded by Barrie Konicov as one of his Potentials Unlimited tape series. You can find information about this tape series on the *thepotentialsunlimited.com* website. Since the time when I used the Potentials Unlimited tape, I have found other tapes that suit me better. But different authors appeal to different people. You might try two or three before you find one you truly love and which is effective for you. Of all tapes I have surveyed, I think the best are the guided imagery tapes prepared by psychologist Belleruth Naparstek. Her tapes are sold on her *healthjourneys.com* website. Words and specially composed music make for strong total effectiveness of these tapes. These tapes are rather "new agey" and not for everyone. You can, however, listen to excerpts on the website to help you make a decision if these tapes would be useful to you. The side of the Belleruth tapes with affirmations (positive statements to reinforce positive attitudes and change) may be more acceptable to you.

One of the problems of eating an extremely low-fat diet is that you often do not feel satisfied until the next meal. The French know the value of including healthy fats in the meal to keep you satisfied until the next mealtime and to prevent snacking. That ounce or one-half ounce of high fat cheese to end the meal can help you feel satisfied. On the other hand, ending a meal with a high carbohydrate, high sugar dessert will often have you craving more food not long after you have finished your meal.

If you find that you are snack hungry before bedtime, even after eating a substantial dinner that includes dessert, try substituting a salad and cheese course following the main course of meat and vegetables for the dessert. Eat a salad of fresh lettuces dressed with extra-virgin olive oil and red wine or balsamic vinegar and about one-half to one ounce of an imported European cheese or quality American-produced cheese (no Kraft or other large corporation cheese food). Skip the high carbohydrate dessert such as cake, pie, cookies, ice cream. Likely you will not want to snack.

Eating a healthy amount of good real food that contains healthy, natural fats and a couple of servings of high fiber vegetables at your meals can prevent the empty feeling that sends you after the chips, candy, and other snacks between meals. Avoiding sugar and too many simple carbohydrates can also sustain your satisfaction.

Much snacking I observe seems to me motivated by greed, that is, a desire for more than one needs, rather than by true hunger. On this topic, philanthropist and writer Brooke Astor wrote in *Vanity Fair* that "To want to enjoy one's dinner is correct, but greed is not. Hunger can be satisfied but greed never can."

And then, greed is not elegant.

Giving up snacking between meals and eating healthy real food seated at meals can help you be as slim and as elegant as chic French women.

How You Do It For Chic & Slim Success:

✂ Give up snacks one snack time at a time.

✂ Use shopping, walking, napping, mineral or bubble baths to distract you from your desire for a snack until your body adjusts to not being fed between meals.

✂ Use prepared or self-scripted self-hypnosis or guided imagery tapes to deal with your snacking problems.

✂ Instead of eating a dessert, end your meal with a salad and cheese course to keep you feeling full and satisfied. Some cheeses you will find on a French cheese platter: Brie, Camembert, St. Andre, Morbier, and, of course, Laughing Cow! (You can find an acceptable quality French brie or camembert in many USA supermarkets today. St. Andre, Morbier, Laughing Cow may be more difficult to find.)

---

chic & slim Email to Anne

Never before has dieting seemed—dare I say it?—so glamorous and exciting.

Eating well is chic and sexy thanks to your insights!

Cynthia in Yonkers

chic & slim Technique 6
MUSIQUE

French women maintain an aura of confident serenity. They eat carefully and slowly. They have energy to conduct their active, busy, and well-ordered lives.

American women are often so rushed in their daily lives that they gobble their food. The pace of their lives renders them too exhausted to exercise. They eat excess calories to give themselves quick energy. They often appear (and feel) harassed.

This technique will help you use certain kinds of music to soothe and heal you so that you will be more serene, help you slow your eating so that you chew carefully and slowly so that you digest your food more properly. You will be slimmer and have more energy for your lifestyle.

The Musique Technique
THE MUSIC TECHNIQUE

Are you stressed? Depressed? Do you eat too quickly? Some days, is it simply impossible to find the energy to exercise?

You can use music as an aid to successfully living the *Chic & Slim* lifestyle.

The work that details the variety of ways music can heal and help you is Don Campbell's *The Mozart Effect: Tapping the Power of Music to Heal the Body, Strengthen the Mind, and Unlock the Creative Spirit.*

Don Campbell sites the pioneering work of French physician Alfred Tomatis. Dr Tomatis's research findings established the healing and creative powers of music, particularly the music of Baroque composer Wolfgang Amadeus Mozart.

The best known of Dr. Tomatis's treatment successes is the French actor Gerard Depardieu. As an aspiring young actor in the mid-1960s, Gerard Depardieu suffered from such severe stammering he had difficulty speaking. With a few months treatment at Dr. Tomatis's clinic, Gerard Depardieu was on his way to the speaking ease and acting success he enjoys today.

The music used in Gerard Depardieu's treatment was that of Mozart. As Dr. Tomatis explained in his book *Pourquoi Mozart? (Why Mozart?)*, Mozart's music has an extraordinary liberating and healing power. The effect of Mozart's music appears to be stronger and more universally effective than the music of other composers.

As Don Campbell writes:

> Clearly, the rhythms, melodies, and high frequencies of Mozart's music stimulate and charge the creative and motivation regions of the brain. But perhaps the key to his greatness is that it all sounds so pure and simple . . . . He is at once deeply mysterious and accessible, and above all without guile. His wit, charm, and simplicity allow us to locate a deeper wisdom in ourselves. To me, Mozart's music is like the great architecture of Moghul India—the Amber Palace in Jaipur, or the Taj Mahal. It is the transparency, the arches, the rhythms within the open space that so profoundly stir the human spirit.

I like Don Campbell's comparison of Mozart's music to jewels of Indo-Islamic architecture. When I lived in India, I became greatly interested in this style of architecture and took advantage of the opportunity to study some of its best known examples located in view of my house. My terrace gave a splendid view of Humayun's Tomb, believed to be the pink marble inspiration for the Taj Mahal. Making the pilgrimage to Agra to see the Taj Mahal was one of the unforgettable experiences of my life.

As I keyboard these words into computer memory, I am listening to Mozart's Andante, K 315 played by flutist James Galway with the Chamber Orchestra of Europe. The music is as exquisitely beautiful as the Taj, that concerto in white marble that points its graceful spires into the Indian sky. From the speakers of my iMac, the music serenades me with a soothing caress that soothes away the distractions and worries and leaves me free to tranlate my thoughts into words.

Even before I read Don Campbell's book, I had discovered that I did my best writing to the slow movements of music by the Baroque composers, particularly Vivaldi, Mozart, Handel, Corelli, and Telemann. I also found New Age music good background for working.

In *The Mozart Effect*, Don Campbell writes that "slower Baroque music (Bach, Handel, Vivaldi, Corelli) imparts a sense of stability, order, predictability, and safety and creates a mentally stimulating environment for study or work." Of New Age music he says, "For people living a highly mental, structured life, such music helps them to unwind and float freely."

Not only were they good for creative work, but I found both Baroque and New Age music excellent music to play during meal or teatime to help me relax and enjoy my food. These lovely melodies put me in a frame of mind to remember to "eat elegantly," taking small bites and chewing each bite slowly and carefully.

Stress-producing and unsettling events are unavoidable in everyday life. Particularly as the background music for my sanity-saving afternoon teatime, I find slow, melodic music wonderful help in disconnecting me from problems and troubles and making possible a retreat. In my sanctuary of calm, I can enjoy a cup of tea and an interesting book or article.

Try to imagine a film without background music. In a film, music can define an ambiance that can make us, the viewers, apprehensive, lighthearted, amorous, frightened, or exploding with laughter. Music can intensify our empathized feelings of passion, joy, longing, and patriotism with the characters on the screen. You can put this mood-enhancing facility of music to work for you to help you fight a depression-induced tendency to seek solace in "comfort foods."

If you have defined one of the factors that works against your health and slimness as overeating when you are feeling blue or depressed, try to treat your "down" feelings with a dose of happy music before you treat yourself to everything in the refrigerator you can stuff into your mouth.

Almost all the classic Broadway musicals have spirit-lifting songs. If that guy who says he is going to call doesn't, it may be the time to sing along with "I'm Gonna Wash that Man Right Outa My Hair," from *South Pacific*. I love all the songs from the musical *The Unsinkable Molly Brown*, and "I Ain't Down Yet" is an especially good one to buck you up from a career setback. I was born and raised in Oklahoma and I have had plenty of experience seeing first hand the state's "beautiful mornings" that are so vividly described in the opening number of *Oklahoma!* I remember struggling through a particularly difficult time of my life. Every morning as I fixed my coffee I would sing the musical's opening number, "Oh, What a Beautiful Mornin'."

The chorus goes: "Oh what a beautiful mornin', oh what a beautiful day. I've got a beautiful feelin' eveything's goin' my way." Everything, of course, did not go my way. But the music gave me a positive attitude that helped me cope with whatever problems and upsets came during the day.

I had already written the above paragraphs when I read *Washington Post* columnist George Will's article about the Broadway revival of *Oklahoma!* George Will points out the play's message is as timely today as we cope with terrorism as it was at the time of its 1943 opening, a dark year in World War II. He quotes historian of Broadway musicals Ethan Mordden who points out that the message in *Oklahoma!* is the unpleasant truth that evil will keep coming at you until you wipe it out. You are going to have to keep coping as best you can with the problems, personal as well as on a global scale. Some good music can keep your spirits up for life's battles.

As careful as I am about nutrition and proper rest for energy, still some days, by the time for my exercise session, I just do not feel as if I possess the energy to walk across the room, much less to put on my walking shoes and go outdoors and walk a couple of miles at a brisk pace, or to make it through an aerobics video.

March music is just that. It is music that has been designed to inspire people to march. Not walk. March. Even when exhausted and battle weary. Move those feet and keep them moving at a brisk pace. Of course the greatest piece of marching music in my opinion is the French national anthem "*La Marseillaise*." Another great national anthem marching song in the same spirit is the Togolese national anthem. As a United States Peace Corps Volunteer to that West African country, I learned the words and tune to that anthem. It is one of those spirited songs that energizes and raises the pride in the singer.

"The Stars and Stripes Forever," "Semper Fidelis," "The Battle Hymn of the Republic," "Anchors Aweigh," all stir us to pick up our feet and move. If you think you are too tired to exercise, put a march tape in the cassette deck or the CD player and march in place to the music. Or use march music to set your pace when you are taking a walk outdoors. You will feel like you are leading a parade. Fun.

Remember that any one type of exercise becomes boring if done every day for years. You need alternatives to your regular exercise to keep exercise pleasurable. Taking your walks or marching in place to march music makes a good alternative exercise. And I have another suggestion.

In addition to marches as inspiration for exercise, when I lived in Corpus Christi, I discovered that Tejano music was great walking music. Tejano is music that evolved when the Mexican-

Americans of South Texas married their mariachi music to the polka beat of the music brought by the area's mid-nineteenth century German settlers. (At least, that is my analysis after listening to Tejano for ten years.) When I lived on the Texas Riviera, I would wear my Sony Walkman to tune in to one of Corpus Christi's Tejano radio stations while I walked laps on the quarter-mile concrete fishing pier behind my condo. If you need something new to motivate you for exercise and have a Walkman or other radio with earphones you can wear when exercising, try it. You may not understand the lyrics in Spanish, but the music will inspire your feet to move.

Music, used creatively, can be a powerful aid in helping you live the *Chic & Slim* lifestyle. If listening to Mozart for a couple of months could turn a stammering Frenchman into one of the world's most successful actors, just think what the proper music, used on a regular basis, might do to help you slow your pace of eating and feel serene and competent to deal with your problems. It can also energize you for exercise when you think you would rather just plop on the sofa and stare at the television.

How You Do It For Chic & Slim Success:

➤ Use calm soothing music as background to your meals to help you eat more slowly and feel more relaxed at mealtime.

➤ Have a collection of happy music to lift your spirits when you feel depressed.

➤ Use music to motivate you to exercise.

➤ Choose exercise videos with good music. You will enjoy your workouts more and be more likely to use these tapes.

➤ Avoid restaurants that use loud, jazzy music to make you eat more food quickly.

Music Resources:

Looking through your own music collection, you may likely find Baroque, New Age, March, and perhaps even Tejano music that you can put to use to help and heal some of your problems. Below are several CDs in my own music collection that I use for just the purposes described in this technique. Of course, there are many more that will likely do as well. Possibly as a result of so many people reading Don Campbell's work you can now buy many recordings that feature only the slow selections of the Baroque composers. Some are devoted to only one composer. Others feature a variety of Baroque composers.

Mozart Adagios Decca (2 CD set) - Time 145:57
This is probably the best "slow Mozart" value for the money. The cover blurb says, "Mozart's slow movements contain some of the most beautiful and peaceful melodies ever written."

Mozart for Relaxation RCA Victor - Playing time 68:01
Familiar pieces exquisitely played. I prefer all instrumental, and don't like the inclusion of one vocal from *Cosi fan tutte*.

Mozart's Music for the Night with Sounds of the River Eclipse Music Corp - Time: 64:22
Sounds of Mozart blended with sounds of a flowing river.

Vivaldi Adagios Decca (2 CD set) - Time: 2 hours+
Soothing and peaceful. Vivaldi's adagios are as beautiful and tranquil as Mozart's.

Beyond the Horizon Real Music - Time: 35 min.
Hilary Stagg's electronically amplified Irish folk harp. Soothing New Age music with a crystal elegance.

Adagio: Music for Silent Moments Arte Nova Time: 78:52
Lovely adagios from Bach, Schubert, Elgar, Holst, and Larsson.

Music for Meditation Vol. 1 Creative Music Time: 56:31
Peaceful classical music at an economical price.

Largo NAXOS Time: 74:45
Slow, tranquil movements by Baroque composers. Lovely.

25 Baroque Favorites Vox Cameo Classics Time: 70+ Min.
Beautiful relaxing, elegant music.

chic & slim Technique 7
RÉSISTANCE

French consumption of refined sugar, though rising, is still somewhere around 19 pounds per person per year. Artificial sweeteners and artificially sweetened food products are not much used. Avoiding large amounts of refined sugar in the French diet helps chic French women stay slim.

The average American consumes more than 140 pounds of sugar per year. Processed, convenience, and low-fat foods have various types of sugar added in the manufacturing. This large (and continually increasing) consumption of sugar fuels the soaring obesity rates in the USA.

The technique will help you lower an excessively high level of sugar consumption to one more in line with that of chic French women so you can lose weight and stay slim. (You may enjoy other health benefits as well.)

La Résistance Technique
THE SUGAR REDUCTION TECHNIQUE

During the occupation of France during World War II, an organization that came to be known as la Résistance fought the invader. In the last several decades, refined sugar has invaded the foods Americans eat. Like those brave French men and women of The Resistance who fought the enemy during the second World War, in order to live the Chic & Slim lifestyle, we must make an effort to fight off the invasion of refined sugar into our diet.

If you want to make one modification in your eating for achieving and maintaining a normal weight and improvement in your general health, reducing a regular high consumption of refined sugar and processed carbohydrates is the one to make.

Reading the labels of many foods sold as a low-fat version of that food, you find that they have substituted various forms of sugar: sugar, corn syrup, dextrose, lactose, maltose, sucrose, or fructose for the fat in the regular version. "Low-fat" cream cheese is one example that comes to mind. In *Chic & Slim Encore*, the second of my *Chic & Slim* books, I analyze a faux fish product prominently labeled "low-fat" that used about five kinds of sugar. By the way, the stuff tasted like fish poached in children's cough syrup.

What's wrong with eating lots of refined sugar?

Studying the subject, I have concluded that if it were easier to understand what happens in our bodies when we consume refined sugar and processed carbohydrates that convert almost instantaneously to sugar, people might more readily realize the dangers and cut their consumption levels.

About as understandable an explanation as any I have read on the problem with refined sugar is in the bestseller *Sugar Busters! : Cut Sugar to Trim Fat*. The authors explain that sugar stimulates the pancreas to secrete insulin. Insulin is needed by our bodies for regulating our blood sugar level, but when our bodies overproduce insulin, we get undesired results. Excess sugar is stored in our bodies as fat. Burning of already stored fat is inhibited. Our livers start making cholesterol that we don't need.

If we eat too much refined sugar, the problems are: (a) we can't burn the fat we already have, (b) we gain even more fat, and (c) cholesterol builds up in our arteries. (Sounds like what has been happening to the health of a lot of people in the USA in the past several decades, doesn't it?)

Eating too much sugar can make us not only overweight, but overweight with heart problems. Oh dear!

I am summarizing and oversImplifying. To get a full explanation you can read the first nine chapters of *Sugar Busters!* And this is probably the place to say that I applaud the book's authors for creating a book that has brought the problem of excessive sugar consumption to the attention of millions of people in the USA. We have a serious, serious problem here. And the authors have offered a detailed solution to this problem. But looking at the French example, I do not think that it is necessary to follow a diet as extreme as *Sugar Busters!* recommends. Certainly not if we look at the health and obesity statistics for the French.

The *Sugar Busters!* program prohibits potatoes, white bread, beets, and carrots (among other foods). As for potatoes, the

French eat about three times as many as Americans. They eat carrots and beets prepared in a variety of ways. (In any case, I really don't think overconsumption of beets and carrots rates at the top of the list of factors in obesity in the USA.) And those wonderful baguettes the French eat are certainly made with white flour, though it is a quality, unbleached white flour. Additionally French bread does not contain sugar and chemicals as much bread consumed in the USA does.

Another point in *Sugar Busters!* with which I am not in complete agreement is their lack of restriction on beverages and foods sweetened with aspartame. The product is sold under a variety of product names and labels. The book's only statement on aspartame that I could find said (in small print on page 126 of my copy of *SugarBusters!*): "Artificial sweeteners are not harmful to the vast majority of individuals. However, they have no nutritional value."

Puritanism in the USA wants people to suffer to lose weight, so when I read articles against the use of some particular diet aid, I always try to evaluate if there really are dangers that have been proven by unbiased scientific testing, or whether the negative media is only Puritanism at work.

As I have written on the *Chic & Slim* website, I have used aspartame very sparingly since it became available. The maximum I used in one day is one packet, and I generally tried to keep use down to 1/3 or 1/2 of those little blue packets in one day, perhaps to add just a bit of sweetness to one of my muffins that I bake without any sugar. If I used aspartame one day, I tried to skip the next day. Once a month I would go at least a week without using aspartame.

But I never felt entirely comfortable with even minimum aspartame use. A number of my friends who have extensive knowledge of chemistry and medicine avoid aspartame as if it were anthrax. (That should have told me something.) In connection with writing this section of the book, I researched the scenario that resulted in the FDA approval of aspartame. What my research uncovered makes me sufficiently uneasy about the approval process for that product that I am very thankful I have been as cautious as I have about my aspartame use. At this time, I am no longer using aspartame.

The French believe that in the long run, using artificial sweeteners will make you eat more sugar instead of less because you will want sweet foods sweeter. Many sweet French foods just aren't as sweet as similar foods in the USA. For instance, the flan I was served in French homes was invariably much less sweet than pudding I ate in American homes.

When I began to observe the French, the most dramatic difference I noticed in the way the French ate and the way that I had always eaten as a fatty was the amount of refined sugar consumed both in foods and in beverages. I was, after all, part of the "Pepsi generation, "and I shudder to remember how many sugared cola soft drinks I consumed as a fatty. Not to mention all that fruit punch served at all those receptions and parties. In our family, there was ample jam or jelly (usually homemade) spread on breakfast toast. Cake, pie, or cookies and ice cream were served after every lunch and dinner. I observed that when the French ate desserts (and a lot of time they didn't), they ate these dinky little servings. Accustomed to large American dessert servings, I found the French-sized servings of desserts disappointingly small.

Another thing I noticed about French desserts was that there was generally protein in the dessert in the form of milk or egg white or nuts. When they drank sugar-sweetened beverages, the French sipped a few fluid ounces slowly. A small glass of beverage would be sipped for hours.

If you live in the USA and you eat much food prepared outside your home, or if you use many prepared or convenience foods, you will have difficulty keeping your sugar consumption as low as the French do. Many commercial foods contain sugar in one form or another. You often see "modified food starch" listed in the ingredients. In *SugarBusters!* the authors say that starch is simply a large sugar molecule. In our digestive tracts starch quickly becomes glucose.   According to that explanation, eating modified food starch seems to produce the same results as eating sugar. It is difficult these days to find a brand of cottage cheese that does not contain modified food starch. On a visit to West Virginia a couple of years ago, I read the label on about fifteen brands and varieties of cottage cheese available in one supermarket's dairy case, trying to find one brand that did not contain modified food starch. Every one contained the ingredient. Here in North Texas I can find one brand that does not contain modified food starch. It is sold by Braum's, a regional dairy.

Read your labels. Know what you are eating. But a warning: it can be scary knowing what processed foods actually contain. And if you want to be really, really terrified, read *Fast Food Nation: The Dark Side of the All-American Meal* by Eric Schlosser. This is a must-read for anyone who eats in the USA.

If you regularly drink sugared soft drinks, lemonades, fruit juices with added sugar, fruit punches, most beers, sweet white wines, the most dramatic reduction in calories from sugar in your diet would be to give up those sugared beverages. Sugar is added in the fermentation process to American wines, I am told. Perhaps that is why I find American wine more intoxicating that a good French wine. The French prefer dry (less sweet) red wines. Americans like sweeter wines, particularly sweet white wines. If you drink wine, you will usually consume less sugar if you drink a dry red wine as the French do rather than a sweet white such as a Zinfandel. In any case, American Zinfandels always taste to me like fermented 7-Up.

One of the first French-inspired modifications I made to my lifestyle was substituting a glass of mineral water with a squeeze of lemon or lime for carbonated cola drinks I had been drinking most of my fatty life. The naturally carbonated mineral waters such as Perrier (French), Apollinaris (German) or San Pellegrino (Italian) make good substitutes for carbonated soft drinks. All these have natural carbonation. If you try to go directly to a nongaseous mineral water such as Evian, it may taste too flat to satisfy. And be warned. Not all bottled waters are mineral waters.

So many bottled waters you find on your supermarket shelf are just filtered tap water put in bottles. Look for the source (you hope it is high in some unpolluted mountains somewhere) and a listing of the mineral content on the label. (Unfortunately not many American mineral waters have these. They just list an 800 number or website where they will answer questions.) If the bottle label says something like filtered tap water from the the water supply of some American city, that is *not* mineral water. You might as well just buy yourself a Brita or a Bodum pitcher and filter your own tap water. It will be a lot cheaper. And you won't be cluttering up the landfill with all those plastic bottles.

Another good substitute for sugared beverages is to drink herbal tea chilled or over ice. I drink herbal teas unsweetened. But even if you add a teaspoon of honey, molasses or sugar to sweeten a glass or cup of the tea, you will be cutting back considerably from the sugar contained in a carbonated cola beverage. Most carbonated soft drinks contain about nine teaspoons of sugar in each 12-ounce can of beverage.

Peppermint tea can be wonderfully refreshing in hot weather, as can lemongrass herbal tea. Lemon verbena grew in my garden when I lived on the Mediterranean. I love a cup of lemon verbena tea and drink it often. Sipping it takes me back to that garden overlooking that blue, blue sea. A friend's favorite hot weather beverage is green tea with peach served over ice. A very elegant tasting drink for a summer afternoon.

Cutting back on cookies, cakes, pies, doughnuts, sweet rolls, ice cream, and candy is such an obvious way to cut your sugar consumption that I feel almost silly mentioning it. But when you cut down on the cookies, cakes, pies, doughnuts, sweet rolls, ice cream, and candy, what are you going to eat in their place? They are obviously important to you, or you probably would not be eating them.

If you have been eating a lot of sugared foods, you are going to have to cut back gradually if you want that reduction to be a permanent change in your diet. If you have read the other *Chic & Slim* books and the postings on the *Chic & Slim* website, you may be weary of me using the word gradually. The reason I keep saying gradually is that is the way our bodies allow us to make changes that become permanent without too much discomfort. If you try to make big changes quickly, your mind and body will fight you. And your mind and body will probably win. You will go back to your well-established, defeating food habits.

On the topic of change made gradually, I offer you this example. Thane Peterson, *Business Week Online* Contributing Editor, made the following observation in one of his weekly Moveable Feast columns, titled "Why So Few French Are Fat." He writes about how Ruth Reichl, editor-in-chief of *Gourmet* magazine, described in a column "how she had always been a bit overweight until one day she decided to eat exactly what she wanted. Miraculously, she gradually lost 30 pounds." Note the word "gradually."

Thane Peterson comments: "As the French have known for years, if what you want to eat is good, fresh food in the company of others, keeping your weight down isn't all that hard for most people."

Please note that he said " . . .if what you want to eat is *good, fresh food. . .*" This is important. If what you want to eat is humongous quantities of nutritionless *junque* food and fast food that include no fresh fruit and no low-calorie green vegetables, and a lot of carbohydrates made from refined white flour, then it will certainly take a miracle for you to lose weight and remain slim permanently.

If you eat commercially made jam on your breakfast bread, you are eating mostly sugar. Today most American brands of factory-made jams and jellies are just corn syrup and sugar with little fruit. You can buy brands of all fruit jams or jellies, though I believe by law they have to be labeled "spreads" or some such thing. These all-fruit jams are generally more expensive than the corn syrup and sugar jams, jellies, and preserves because it is much less expensive to put corn syrup, food color and pectin in a jar than fruit. Also you do not have to wash, peel, seed, and chop corn syrup, food color, and pectin.

In the typical French kitchen, you find jars of homemade jams and preserves lined up on a shelf. The French make these *confitures* from fresh or dried fruit and sweeten them with grape or apple juice to make an all-fruit recipe. I have recipes for a quick microwave version of this jam in both the *Chic & Slim* books. If you don't use a microwave, you can cook it on top of the stove using traditional jam making techniques included in any standard cookbook.

For breakfast I often eat a wedge of my Barone Breakfast Bread. (Recipe included in *Chic & Slim Encore.*) This bread is made without any sugar of any kind and is based on Irish soda bread. Eating too much of products made with wheat has been shown to interfere with metabolism; so I have been making my bread using a combination of other flours: whole grain rye, whole grain soy, spelt, buckwheat, corn, old fashioned rolled oats, and ground flax seed. I always bake this bread in my old-faithful cast-iron skillet. This recipe makes a heavy, stick-to- your-ribs bread that I spread with butter or a nut butter. Almond or walnut can be heavenly. And for a while, I even became rather fond of sunflower seed butter, though I never thought of it as heavenly. Just a sort of nutty taste. Sunflower seed butter was much cheaper than almond or walnut butter. And I was feeling frugal.

Sometimes in place of butter on my breakfast bread, I use a basic white goat cheese or a Mexican cheese, *queso fresco* and top this with one of my homemade all-fruit jams. When I visited my son, his neighborhood supermarket sold a nice Danish feta that was good breakfast eating spread on whole wheat sourdough. Ricotta cheese is also good for spreading on your breakfast bread. Some people like cream cheese. For some reason I just don't like cream cheese. At least I do not like most American brands of cream cheese. These taste to me like white spreadable plastic. Many who avoid dairy like yogurt cheese on Barone Breakfast Bread or other morning breads. Yogurt cheese is easy to make from plain yogurt if you have a tea strainer lined with a couple of coffee filters.

For afternoon tea, I make a variety of sugarless pastries. I make oatmeal and other muffins without sugar and then sprinkle on a bit of sweetener or top with all fruit jam. I also make a sugarless coffeecake, a wedge of which can be topped with ricotta or cottage cheese and fresh fruit. More and more I am finding that I like a sandwich rather than a pastry with my afternoon tea. Curried chicken salad, egg salad, tomato and cheese, or the traditional cucumber and butter sandwich for tea are good. All these sandwiches are delicious made with rye or whole grain bread.

Since I rarely eat dessert at the end of a meal, this sometimes creates a potential problem when I am eating a meal in someone else's home. If the hostess or host has gone to a great deal of effort to create a spectacular dessert, she (or he) may be unhappy when I refuse what has taken so much time and effort to create. I will often ask my hostess or host if I can take my serving home with me. Of course, these party desserts are invariably made with lots of sugar. I can reduce the amount of sugar I consume in my afternoon tea pastry by scraping off the frosting and then topping a half or third of the serving of cake with cheese of some sort and fresh fruit. If the dessert is pie, I only eat half or third of the serving and top that with cheese and fresh fruit. If it is a fruit pie, I will sometimes only add cheese. A good sharp Wisconsin cheddar, or its English cousin Cheshire is wonderful on apple or pear pie. Cheshire is an old cheese (it has been around since the 12th century) and a bit firmer and more crumbly than cheddar. I prefer it to cheddar, especially with fruit. Feta (one that is not too salty) is good crumbled on peach or berry pie.

Of course I keep a great deal of sugar out of my diet by avoiding processed foods, mixes, and other *faux* and *junque* foods. Like the French, I usually eat at home. Also like the French, I keep fast food to a minimum. But there is a dairy store near me that, if I catch the right woman of a certain age on the kitchen shift, she makes me a lovely hamburger on which she piles lots of lettuce and tomato slices on the crisply cooked meat. She puts just the amount of mayonnaise that I like. Once a month or so I will treat myself to one of these burgers when I have been out shopping. I will bring this burger home and eat it with sliced cucumber or raw zucchini and then fresh fruit for dessert. While I am not rigid about what I eat, for the most part I eat food I have prepared myself from fresh, natural ingredients. And I always try to relax and enjoy the good food I prepare.

Though I often blame advertising for causing Americans

to overeat foods they would best avoid, one positive change in American eating habits resulted from food advertising. Those clever advertisements for Pace Picante Sauce (The weathered Texas cowboys tasting the inferior sauce and saying with a grimace, "This stuff was made in New York City!") weaned many Americans away from highly sugared ketchup, replacing it with an unsugared condiment that contained vegetables. In fact, according to an *austinchronicle.com* posting, by 1992, salsa had replaced ketchup as America's number one condiment. Thank you, Pace of San Antonio.

The good news is that if you make an effort to cut back on the refined sugar in your diet, your body will help you. I eat so little refined sugar now that when I do eat an American size serving of pie or cake, I feel so ill afterward that the memory of how miserable I was stops me when I am again tempted to so injudiciously indulge.

One more morsel of "Anne Barone's voice of experience" advice. The amount of refined sugar in my diet is now very low. But sometimes I find that I am eating more sugared foods. (This can happen during the Thanksgiving to New Year's holiday season.) I look in my cupboard and see a package of cookies there that I have occasionally eaten as my pastry with my afternoon tea when I had nothing better available. Only three cookies left, I observe. So this idea pops into my head that I will just eat those cookies and get rid of them. Banish temptation in one quick effort.

Do I need to tell you that this eat-it-up-to-get-rid-of-it is a *very bad* idea? If you are tempted to eat a large quantity of sugared foods in an effort to rid the pantry of them, don't. Throw those cookies or cupcakes or whatever in the garbage. Be sure it is the yucky part of the garbage from which you will not dare fish it out. Eating up the supply of cookies or cake or whatever that is left so you can start a virtuous, sugar-free tomorrow is a very bad idea. Anne Barone's voice of experience speaks.

How You Do It For Chic & Slim Success:

⤙ Identify which foods and beverages are adding large amounts of sugar to your daily food intake.

⤙ Gradually begin to eliminate major sources of sugar in your diet.

⤙ Look to all-fruit jams and to breads and muffins made without sugar to replace the bread and jam you have been eating.

⤙ Read the first nine chapters of *Sugar Busters!* for an explanation of precisely what happens in the body when you consume large amount of sugar.

⤙ Let you body be your ally in eliminating sugar from your diet.

⤙ Like French women, instead of carbonated soft drinks, have a glass of mineral water with a squeeze of lemon or lime, or drink a chilled herbal tea.

⤙ End your meals with about one-half to one ounce of high fat cheese rather than a highly-sugared dessert.

And then there is stevia . . .

Stevia is a natural plant product used for centuries in South America and, for the past 30 years, in Japan, to replace sugar for sweetness in various dishes. Neither the Paraguayans nor the Japanese seem to have suffered for this use. The American sugar lobby is powerful, and so are business interests for artificial sweeteners currently marketed in the USA. The way these powerful interests are able to influence government regulations may explain the FDA official unwillingness to classify stevia as a sweetener. On the other hand, it is a natural plant product used for centuries and not some Frankenfood product cooked up in some chemistry lab in recent decades as are many of those products sold as "sweeteners."

Americans are just beginning to try this product now available in health food stores and from online health food product websites. Cooking with stevia, particularly baking, is reportedly tricky. A number who have experimented with trying to substitute the substance into traditional recipes that use refined sugar recommend using recipes specifically written for stevia. A quick search on *Amazon.com* turned up four stevia cookbooks.

And article in *USA Today* titled "A Sweet Alternative: Raising stevia instead of cane," by Shawn Sell, reported on the growing popularity of this product. The article quotes Ray Sahelian, a general practitioner in Marina Del Ray, California, and co-author of *The Stevia Cookbook: Cooking With Nature's Calorie-Free Sweetener*. He points out that Americans are uncomfortable with our choices of artificial sweeteners and are looking for safe, natural alternatives prompting the use of stevia.

The botanical name of this plant native to Paraguay is *Stevia rebaudiana*, and it is the sweetest known natural substance. Please note that it is a natural plant substance. According to the *USA Today* article, stevia leaves are 10 to 15 times as sweet as table sugar, but extracts range from 100 to 300 times as sweet. "Proponents say it contains virtually no calories, doesn't raise blood-sugar levels or promote tooth decay, and lacks the chemical aftertastes of many artificial sweeteners."

My experience with stevia has been limited, but basically positive. The first stevia I bought was in powder form in packets. In addition to the *Stevia rebaudiana* Extract, the product also contained rice maltodextrin and silica. Rice maltodextrin, it seems, is rice syrup solids. That sounds like a kind of sugar to me. The second brand of stevia in individual packets I bought contained stevia leaf extract and erythritol, used as a natural filler. You can also purchase powdered as well as liquid stevia leaf extract in the pure form. The advantage of added ingredients is that when the stevia extract is in the pure form, it is difficult to measure out a sufficiently tiny amount. Stevia extract is very, very sweet.

In a health food store, I purchased liquid stevia extract. This product worked well for sweetening, but I was uncomfortable that it contained 18% alcohol. I have since discovered that it is possible to buy stevia in liquid form that contains no alcohol. The one brand I tried looks like watery molasses. I do not find it as effective for sweetening as the powdered forms of stevia. You can find stevia for sale in an assortment of forms in many natural food stores and from online merchants.

As for the sweetening ability of the versions of stevia I have tried, all were far better tasting than saccharin. Initially I did not find stevia as satisfyingly sweet as either granulated cane sugar or aspartame. But as a friend reminded me, initially, any of the sugar replacements require becoming accustomed to their particular taste. That seems to be true of stevia whose taste I am finding more acceptably sweet the longer I use it.

I have not yet used stevia much as a sugar substitute in baking. But I did substitute stevia for half of the sugar in a whole wheat brownie recipe that I had created some years ago. I was happy with the taste of these brownies containing stevia. Eventually I should be able to modify the recipe so that I use all stevia for sweetness in this recipe.

The powdered form of stevia seems to be preferable for baking and sprinkling atop muffins, cakes, or cookies made without sugar. I think the liquid version sweetens beverages better. Stevia produces the most cane sugar-like sweetness when added to acidic fruits or beverages.

If you are looking for an alternative to saccharin or aspartame, you might try stevia.

chic & slim Email to Anne

Dear Anne,

Thank you very much for sending out my order of your two books so quickly. I wasn't quite sure what to expect from your books. However your books (along with some of my own research) have already made a major difference in my life and my family's life in just one week.

I have stopped dieting or counting calories. I shop now for "real" food. My husband and I sit down at the table for more leisurely family breakfasts and dinners now. We have a small half glass of red wine with dinner instead of soda pop.

In one week:

- I have lost 3 pounds.

- My husband seems happier and less stressed.
- I feel closer to my husband since we talk at breakfast and dinnertime.
- I'm sleeping better and my sleep problems seem to be gone.
- I have more energy and time to play with my active baby daughter.

All this and more without one bit of dieting!

I am looking forward to implementing more of your commonsense, helpful tips in the future. You don't know how thankful I am that I found your books by accident during a web search. Please ignore your critics and keep up the good work. I feel it is only a matter of time before your books will become word-of-mouth bestsellers.

Best Wishes,
Paula in New York

chic & slim Technique 8
RÉALITÉ

French women are realistic about life, about food, about health, and most of all about men. Seeing things and dealing with them as they really are cuts down on frustration and makes them happier and slimmer.

American women are often taken in by thehype of quick weight loss plans and gimmicks. Many try to change men rather than accepting men as they really are. Often American women avoid the realities about people and situations. Avoiding realities in their life, they often become angry and frustrated and seek solace in food.

This technique is designed to help you deal with the realities of food, of situations, of people in general and men in specific in your life, so that you will be happier and slimmer. And much more chic.

The Réalité Technique
THE REALITY TECHNIQUE

A few years ago, counting calories was the weight control method *du jour*. One bit of humor that made the rounds then was a list usually titled something like "Calories That Don't Count." I do not remember the entire list, but they were things such as the peanut butter you licked off the spoon, the half sandwich left on your toddler's plate, chocolate eaten in the dark.

The humor here (or stupidity, depending on your perspective) was that many Americans following a diet program that required counting calories were not adding into their daily totals calories they kidded themselves "did not really count."

French women would fail to see humor in such a list. They would think that believing that eating certain high calorie foods under certain conditions, such as in the dark, made them calorie-free was idiotic. *Ils sont fous ces Américains!* They're crazy, those Americans.

Yet when it comes to weight control, I continue to be astounded at how many Americans kid themselves about the realities, and how, seeking the easy miracle, they buy the hype. And they buy the gimmicks. $30 billion a year spent on weight control products in the USA. Many of these products are useless, others are dangerous. And despite all the books, tapes, videos, supplements, diet pills, Americans are getting fatter, and fatter.

Why are Americans less willing than people of other nations to accept the reality of a situation? I think there are historic reasons. If those who settled this country and turned wilderness into a productive, prosperous nation had focused closely on the realities of the situation, they would likely have stayed in the countries from which they came. If those pioneers in their covered wagons setting out for the western frontier had been realistic about the difficulties and dangers and possible death that lurked in the mountains and deserts, few would ever have ventured out to settle the West. Optimistic avoidance of reality is great for turning harsh, dangerous wilderness into a prosperous, developed nation. But in the 21st century with the geographic frontier tamed, optimistic avoidance of reality about what you are feeding your body can make and keep you fat. It can undermine your health. Avoidance of reality can keep you from having meaningful and successful relationships.

After the attacks on 11 September 2001, many thoughtful people wrote that, in those attacks, Americans had lost their innocence. A better way of stating it was that Americans could no longer go on avoiding certain realities. We had to face the reality that the oceans east and west and the friendly neighbors north and south no longer gave us the protection it once did. We had to stop believing the comfortable myths we had created about our security. We had to face the fact that there were some pretty dangerous people in the world who really, really do not like the USA.

Most of the approximately 60% of the population of the USA who are overweight have not yet had a similar wakeup call. They heard the TV anchorwoman read the lead to the story about the US Surgeon General declaring excess weight and obesity a national epidemic and picked up the remote control and switched to The Weather Channel.

Too many of those who have determined to try to do something to take off excess pounds are buying the weight control books that offer one extreme gimmick or another. Others think charging a StairMaster to their VISA card will do the trick. They somehow neglect the reality that they are actually going to have to workout on the StairMaster on a regular basis to get any results.

So why not face the reality that, instead of extreme programs and expensive equipment, you just need to stop overeating a lot of processed and convenience food and exercise 30 minutes a day about five days a week? Is that just too simple?

Many women who do face the reality about food and weight control are still unrealistic about men. As I have written repeatedly, French women accept men as they are. Many American women have the idea that they can change men to the way they think men should be. History, psychology, and biology indicate men are not very changeable.

And when men do not change to the way women want them to be, the frustration that results often drives these women to overeating.

One of the people writing the most logically and sensibly about the benefits of being more realistic about people and situations in your life is the psychologist Nathaniel Branden. Two of his books deal specifically with this topic: *The Art of Living Consciously* and *Taking Responsibility*.

In *Taking Responsibility*, Dr. Branden has an excellent chapter, "Self-Responsibility and Romantic Love." He discusses how women often avoid the unpleasant facts about the men with whom they are involved, thinking they will be happier that way. But, in fact, these women remain miserable and distraught.

In contrast, he quotes a woman who told him, "An hour after I met the man I married I could have given you a lecture on ways he would be difficult to live with." But she adds, "He's the most exciting man I have ever known. But I've never kidded myself about the fact the he's also one of the most self-absorbed."

She says that she had to realize and accept what she was getting into when she married him, or she would have been upset later. But is she upset? No, she says, "I've never been happier in my whole life than I am right now in this marriage."

She faced the reality of what her marriage was going to be. And nowhere in her statement that Dr. Branden quotes is there the slightest suggestion that she has any thoughts of changing her husband. She looked at the total package and thought that the positives outweighed the negatives.

For an example of a woman who went into marriage avoiding the realities of the situation and experienced great frustration because of it, I can think of few better public examples than Diana, Princess of Wales. As the unhappy saga of the relationship between the Princess and her husband Prince Charles played out in the media, I could not help thinking how much of her anguish might have been avoided— and how much better training for life as the wife of the future king of England it would have provided—if, instead of working as a baby-sitter for an American family in London, she had spent a year or so in Paris working as an *au pair* for a French family. French women would have shown Diana by example how to accept the realities of the men with whom you are involved.

It always seemed to me that perhaps Diana believed the premise in all those romance novels written by her step-grandmother, the author Barbara Cartland. In these novels the "prince" who has had many lovers falls so passionately in love with the beautiful young woman that he marries her and pledges his fidelity for the rest of their days.

Barbara Cartland sold a zillion books and became very rich authoring books built on that romantic premise. But actual historical evidence does not suggest monogamy as a usual practice of British royalty. Had she faced this reality, might not Diana have made a decision that she could or could not live with the realities of marriage to a royal prince and given her answer accordingly? If you listen to that famous interview Princess Diana gave to the BBC, you feel that her fantasy of what marriage to Charles would be like was far stronger than the reality indicated by history and by what anyone could have learned about Prince Charles from the extensive media coverage of the man.

We know from Diana's own public statements that she experienced much mental anguish which led to problems with health and with food as her marital unhappiness grew.

Apparently I am not alone in believing a French attitude toward her marriage might have aided Princess Diana in her dealings with her husband. I received an email from a woman well familiar with the *Chic & Slim* French-inspired philosophy who, after seeing a television film on the royal marriage, wrote:

> While I certainly do not justify some of Prince Charles's actions, I wondered to myself if only Princess Diana had handled him in a French manner, never demanded, never made accusations about Camilla Parker-Bowles, instead charmed him, stayed calm instead of having hysterics etc. that perhaps history would have been very different.

People often confuse facing reality with pessimistic thinking. Facing reality neither sees things worse

90 — chic & slim TECHNIQUES

(pessimistically) nor better (optimistically). Facing reality is simply looking at things as they *are*.

Another reason people avoid reality is they are afraid of the pain facing reality will bring. They think that it would be better not to know the truth. In fact, avoiding the facts of situations and about people brings the difficulties in most cases. For instance, there are women who insist that their problem with excess weight is hereditary. Often what they "inherited" is their family's habit of eating large servings of dessert at the end of every lunch and dinner and a big bowl of ice cream before going to bed. If they faced the realistic facts about the situation, these women would realize that it was their consumption of more food than their bodies required (much of it nutritionless refined sugar) that was causing their excess weight.

There are women who, as young girls, were told by their mothers, or their cousins, or their next door neighbor that they were unattractive. They continue to believe this as adult women. But if they were realistic about their features, they would realize that there is nothing wrong with their looks. All they need is a better haircut, new eyeglass frames that suit them better (or contact lenses), altering their skirt length to a more flattering one, and trading their comfortable shoes for a stylish well-made pair of mid-heel pumps or some sexy sandals. Probably better posture would also help. In many cases, being told as a child that you are unattractive is a real posture killer in the adult woman.

And now there are an astounding number of safe and reasonably priced cosmetic procedures that can correct facial and figure flaws. I have recently researched some of these looking for the best treatment for a nose scar and an adjacent vein that broke during a walk I had to make outdoors in extremely cold temperatures a number of years ago. I noted, by the way, that many of these machines and related treatments were developed in France.

Americans also refuse to face certain realities about food. I knew a woman in the 1960s who insisted that Sprite was a diet soft drink. None of us could convince her that Sprite contained sugar, and if she wanted a non-cola carbonated beverage, she would do better to choose Fresca. She continued to drink Sprite and was only mildly puzzled when, instead of losing weight, she actually gained about 10 pounds. Read the labels of the foods and beverages you eat and drink.

In his book *The Art of Living Consciously*, Nathaniel Branden stresses that people learn to avoid reality because experiences as children forced them to do so in order to survive bad parenting. Yet he says that the benefits of being conscious of the true facts of a situation are well worth the fantasies one gives up. "In aligning ourselves with reality as we understand it, we optimize our chance for success. And in setting ourselves against reality, we condemn ourselves to failure."

The sultry Latin beauty Bianca Jagger said, "It is when you understand yourself, really know who you are emotionally, mentally, and physically, that real beauty emerges." Knowing yourself requires being realistic. So to achieve real beauty, too, requires being realistic.

You can greatly increase your chance for being slim, healthy, happy, attractive, and successful if you avoid kidding yourself, and if you accept and deal with realities in your own life.

How You Do It For Chic & Slim Success:

➳ Ask yourself in what areas of your life you are avoiding the realities about food, about people, about yourself?

➳ If you are afraid of certain realities, ask yourself what might happen if you were to accept the reality of the situation, what would you do differently than you are doing now? If you approached the situation differently, might the situation improve?

➤ Do not allow people's perceptions of people and situations to determine your own understanding of people and situations. Make your own analysis and make up your own mind about what the reality is. Get facts, not opinions.

➤ Accept the reality that quick weight loss schemes and gimmicks only work in the short term. If you are overweight, in the long term, you are going to have to modify your lifestyle if you are going to lose weight and stay slim and healthy. And take it from someone who modified her lifestyle, the rewards are definitely worth the efforts to change.

Frenchwomen have been in the professions for years—as doctors, lawyers, professors, writers, businesswomen—without threatening their men nor relinquishing one iota of their feminine appeal in exchange for success. . . . At her best, the Frenchwoman is a compendium of worldliness, chic, charm, mystery, and subtlety who realizes that a feminine woman can create an aura of beauty without being beautiful at all and can do whatever she pleases as long as she does it with taste and discretion.

Diane de Dubovay
on Femininity in Vogue

FINDING BACKGROUND BOOKS & ARTICLES

In this, as well as in other *Chic & Slim* books, I quote a number of books and articles. Often readers are interested in reading the entire publication in which I found the quoted material. Locating these books and articles is not always easy. Books go out of print quickly, and though some web articles are archived on the publication's websites, others are not. My collection of newspaper and magazine clippings which I use as background materials goes back a couple of decades. To help you find books and articles I quote in the *Chic & Slim* books, I offer the following suggestions:

For those web articles that are archived, you can find many of them by doing a search on *Google.com*. Magazine articles can be found in back issues kept in public and university libraries. Also, many magazines sell their back issues. See the magazine's website or call their subscription 800 number for information. Many libraries keep back issues of newspapers on microfilm.

Of course, books currently in print can be found in bookstores and on *Amazon.com*. Out-of-print books can be found in used book stores or from the used book dealers who list their merchandise on the catalog pages on *Amazon.com*. You can also find most out-of-print books on my favorite used book website, *abebooks.com*.

More information about the sources of quotes in *Chic & Slim Techniques* can be found on the supporting website for the *Chic & Slim* books, *annebarone.com*.

chic & slim Technique 9
FÉMINITÉ

French women are known for their ultra femininity. They have not made great feminist demands for "equality." French women find their femininity an aid to staying slim.

American women in the past several decades have largely given up femininity for "equality." During these same decades the percentage of the US population that is obese has increased 60 percent.

This technique aims to define femininity and suggest its value for women who want to be chic, slim, and enjoy satisfying relationships.

⌒

The Féminité Technique
THE FEMININITY TECHNIQUE

Femininity is the quality of being womanly. French women are known for being the *plus femme*, the most feminine women in the world. They have raised femininity to an art form: *l'art de femme*, the art of being women. Their femininity, rather than costing them in the workplace, seems to pay dividends.

Karen Fawcett, president of *bonjourParis.com*, wrote in an article on that website: "In France, it's OK for women to look sexy." But, she explains, "French women don't wear see all/ show all clothes to the office. However, don't be surprised if you encounter a female bank executive wearing a dark suit with a short and tightly fitted skirt, a silk blouse showing a bit of décolleté and very high-heeled shoes." Karen Fawcett adds that, with few exceptions, in France, executive women are taken seriously. They don't have the kind of sexual harassment laws in the workplace we have in the USA because French women "are perfectly capable of fending for themselves."

French femininity is neither lacking in intelligence, nor weak and helpless. Quite often these very feminine French women are perfectly capable of hoisting a wrench and unplugging a stopped-up sink, and still looking adorably feminine as they do so.

Certainly what she choses to wear is an important element

in French women's femininity. But even when actively participating in sports, French women usually manage to make themselves look feminine. Recently I was looking at a snapshot of two young Frenchmen and two young Frenchwomen on an Alpine hiking jaunt. They had stopped to pose for someone's camera. The young women were wearing jeans, hiking boots, a pullover sweater, and caps. I have seen numerous photos of a hiking excursion that included young American men and women. Why did these French women look so much more feminine than the young American women I have often seen in hiking photos?

First of all, these young women were chicly slim (so often American women these days are chunky) and their jeans were worn very tight and rolled just so to just below the knee leaving an expanse of shapely calf between the top of the boot and the pant. Their sweaters clung so that they showed their bust to advantage, and the caps on their heads sat at just the right angle. They looked into the camera so sure of their attractiveness. Ah, that element of French confidence does so much for attractiveness. More than anything they look comfortable in their own skin and pleased with being women.

In *The Parisian Woman's Guide to Style*, Parisian mother and daughter Virginie and Véronique Morana show us those chic feminine clothes that enhance and define French women's femininity. One section "Lingerie: Quintessential Feminine Allure" begins: "Marked by elaborate detail and fine fabrics, good-quality French lingerie tends to be fairly expensive." The authors define the various categories of French lingerie according to price and style. The list begins at the top. "The quintessential name in Parisian lingerie, Christian Dior, is the most luxurious—and most expensive."

An introduction I often use when I give talks to women's groups about *Chic & Slim:* I hold up an aerobic exercise videocassette and say: "American women find this product useful for weight control." Then I hold up a Christian Dior lavender lace underwire bra and say: "While American women find an aerobic exercise videocassette useful for weight control, French women find pretty feminine lingerie useful for weight control." That is the best way I know to briefly explain the different approaches French women and American women have for staying slim.

French women often invest in quality lingerie. They believe it pays rich dividends in how they feel about themselves as women. Even when no one else sees it. Though these women are very good at deft little movements so that some of their lingerie just happens to show. For instance, when they bend down to pick up Fido, a jacket falls open in such a way to give a glimpse of the bodice of a lacy slip.

In the USA today, you can buy feminine, lacy, well-made lingerie for reasonable prices. You can use it as a secret weapon for feeling feminine.

Care of their bodies to keep them soft and pretty is also a strong element in French women's femininity. Diane Johnson, in her Paris-based novel *Le Mariage,* describes the young French woman Anne-Sophie d'Argel:

> Anne-Sophie, at home in her small apartment on the rue Saint-Dominique was preparing to bathe. Rosy and compact, her breasts were the little pink-tipped breasts of a Boucher nymph. . . . Nipples just peeking out of the suds. . . polished toe surfacing at the faucet end. Anne-Sophie lined up the stuff she used for her elaborate baths: bath oil, soap, shampoo, rinse, *crème de gommage,* razor, pumice.

Diane Johnson tells us that Anne-Sophie believes in paying attention to the *petits soins*, the little personal care details that keep a woman pretty and feminine.

A bit later she writes about Anne-Sophie's attitude toward her upcoming marriage to a young American journalist: "Anne-Sophie had a Frenchwoman's sense of vocation—but she was also an expert in hunting prints and a very good businesswoman." Anne-Sophie had a very strong French sense of her vocation as wife, but that in no way precluded her from having a successful and interesting career.

What aids a woman's femininity? What diminishes it? We already see from some of the above examples that practicing the French brand of femininity certainly does not stop a woman from holding an executive position, nor from running her own business. So. Is femininity basically a few well chosen accessories, valuing oneself enough to take care of one's body with regular grooming, and believing that an appearance and personality pleasing to men is a useful aid to achieving one's own happiness?

I received an email from a woman who had bought and read both *Chic & Slim* books. In her letter, she included the paragraph:

> In addition to helping me lose weight, you have also helped me reconnect with my femininity. Throughout my weight problems, I've still felt attractive, but not especially feminine. Now I'm taking the extra time in the morning to put on some pearl earrings or a sparkly pin. Just an extra touch to give me that "chic" edge.

How does a woman make herself more feminine? In the Irving Berlin musical *Annie Get Your Gun*, the character Frank

Butler, based on the real life husband of legendary markswoman and show personality Annie Oakley, defines the traits of a feminine woman in a song, "The Girl That I Marry." As I write this, I am listening to Tony-nominated Broadway star Tom Wopat sing the song on the soundtrack of the 1999 Broadway Revival of *Annie Get Your Gun,* in which Bernadette Peters played the title role. The list of femininity traits from the song seem very much in sync with French femininity.

Beginning the list is the declaration that a feminine woman is *soft and pink.* That would certainly mean caring for the skin, especially the face, not to mention keeping after the feet with a pumice stone. French women do not neglect their feet. They also keep the whole body smooth with careful scrubbing with a brush or loofah. It takes such little time and feels so good, not to mention what a positive payoff you have in smoother, healthier skin.

The song goes on to say that a woman would *wear satins and laces and smell of cologne.* Satins and laces are often the fabrics of choice in the lingerie French women wear to make them feel pretty and feminine. And a French woman feels undressed without her scent. Helene Rochas said perfume was the "music of the heart." Scent lingers longest in the memory.

Her nails will be polished and in her hair *she wears a gardenia.* French women give great care to their hands and to their nails, though if they opt for nail polish, it will most likely be clear or a pale color. They think dark colors of nail polish might chip and look tacky. But they do usually polish the nails on their well-pumiced, pretty toes in a bright color. Red is a classic choice. One way French women add a note of femininity, even when they are wearing very severe styles such as jeans and a man's shirt, is some adornment for their hair: a hair ribbon, a bow, a barrette or clasp, a colorful scarf as a headband, or even a fresh flower.

She'll purr like a kitten. French women know the power of a pleasing, seductive voice to charm a man. And they are careful to keep their laughter soft and ladylike. No guffaws, chortles, or cackles. That wouldn't be feminine. A sexy little giggle, however, is another matter.

A doll I can carry. Oh dear! In my fatty days, hearing that last feminine trait listed in the song used to depress me. I was definitely too heavy for any man to lift, at least without serious back strain. But, of course, French women keep themselves slim enough to be easily lifted in a man's arms and carried.

Different men find different feminine elements alluring. Some like polished nails. Some want their wives and girl friends to wear long hair even when hair down below their shoulders is not particularly flattering to these women. Flattering doesn't seem to be the point. So it probably makes sense for these women to go ahead and wear the unflattering hairstyle if it makes the men with whom they have a relationship happy.

Sometimes what a particular man will want the woman in his life to wear is just tacky taste. (Some American men have really awful taste.) For a woman of good taste this poses a dilemma which requires some diplomacy. One would hope that this hazard could be negotiated without having to choose between wearing something tacky or finding another man.

French models of femininity abound. Catherine Deneuve and Anouk Aimee are *ne plus ultra* examples we have been observing for decades. Lately we have been entranced by actress Audrey Tautou, who so delectably portrays the lead in the film *Amelie: The fabulous destiny of Amelie Poulain.*

But femininity is more than keeping your toes pumiced, your nails buffed, your lingerie silky, your hair ribboned, and cultivating a pleasing voice. Feeling womanly is a state of mind. And French women find it a most pleasurable and effective state of mind. French femininity is a potent force in their battle against fat. *Vive la femme!*

How You Do It For Chic & Slim Success:

➤ If you don't have one, learn a skin care program appropriate to your skin type. A good reference is *Bobbi Brown Beauty* by makeup artist Bobbi Brown.

➤ Like French women, spend more on skin care than on makeup to cover up skin problems.

➤ Like French women, understand that what you eat and whether or not you exercise regularly will make more difference in your skin than what you rub on it.

➤ Invest in a bath brush or a loofah to keep your body exfoliated and smooth. Buy them in any drugstore or discount store.

➤ Keep your nails filed and your hands soft with lotion. Especially if you have to have your hands in water a great deal or you handle paper a lot (paper is drying) be sure to have hand lotion handy to apply often to your hands. Bathroom, bedroom, kitchen, desk, car, purse.

➤ Run your fingernails over a bar of soap before gardening. The soap keeps the dirt out and washes out easily with water and a nail brush when your gardening is finished.

➤ Buy a pumice stone to keep your feet smooth. Get the real stone not the fiberglass version.

➤ No matter what else you have on, make sure that you have one feminine element in your outfit.

➤ Choose and wear a signature scent. Even some of the less expensive colognes or eau de toilettes have lovely fragrances.

➤ Make pretty lingerie your secret weapon to make you feel attractive and pretty.

➤ Tailor your femininity to the man in your life (or the sort of man you would like to have in your life). Observe him watching other women to see what attracts him.

➤ A relaxed, genuine smile that reflects the true contentment you feel with your life is the best thing you can put on your face.

chic & slim Technique 10
TOUJOURS

French women always dress carefully before going out, even if only for a quick trip to the corner bakery for a baguette. They always look chic. French women always eat sensibly and moderately. They stay slim.

American women, at times, dress with great care and style, at other times, they neglect their appearance. American women, at times, maintain rigid diet regimes; at other times, they indulge in eating binges. Many American women struggle with excess weight.

This technique will help you become more disciplined and consistent at your *Chic & Slim* efforts. You will likely be slimmer and more consistently maintain a chic appearance.

⌒

The Toujours Technique
THE CHIC & SLIM ALWAYS TECHNIQUE

French women know that a perverse law operates in the universe.

The law states that if only once in one hundred times you do *not* do something, that will be the one time that it was important that you *do* it.

You can go out with your makeup well applied 364 days a year, but the *one* day that you decide that you can dash out for a quick trip to the convenience store without even bothering with lipstick, that will be the day you encounter (a) the man you most want to see you at your best, (b) your worst enemy who will tell all over town how awful you looked, (c) your always impeccably dressed great aunt who will be very disappointed in your appearance and decide to leave her Waterford crystal to your cousin instead of you. On a really bad day, you will encounter all of the above mentioned individuals.

Generally you eat at mealtime and seated. But on the day that you have a five o'clock meeting, you haven't had time for lunch and you are starving. So as you take the elevator to the 22nd floor, you try to eat a tuna sandwich on the way to the meeting. Of course, just as your mouth is really full, the elevator door opens and into the elevator steps the supervisor who will make your next performance evaluation. You can't even say hello through the wad of fish and mayonnaise in your mouth.

Such a stress-producing situation never happens to French women. They always go out neatly dressed, with their hair arranged and makeup perfect. They would never even think of eating while they were walking. (The poor digestion, how it would suffer! You would not have pleasure in your meal.)

In Dorothy Adelson's book, *Roughing It On the Rue de la Paix,* she describes her French friend Simone as her "model par excellence of the *femme élégante.*" She writes of Simone: "Deeply and irretrievably coquette, Simone would have dressed, massaged, beauty-masqued and creamed to the nines if alone on a desert island."

Mais oui. But, of course, says the chic French woman. Because as everyone knows, *ma chère,* ships sometimes pass by desert islands. And on ships you are most likely to find men. And if a ship passed by, the men aboard would not bother to rescue an unattractive woman. Ah, but one they found pleasing to the eye, they would bring her on board and treat her like a queen as they carried her back over the seas to France.

That is how French women think. These women have their own best interests in mind. Consequently a French woman would always take care of her personal appearance even if she were alone on a desert island.

A personal story. Several years ago I was hospitalized for major surgery. Every morning around 6:00 AM, the doctor came by on his morning rounds. Having been indoctrinated in the Always Principle by French women, I made it a point to put on my makeup and have my hair combed by the time the doctor arrived in my room.

I was still attached to an IV, and to go into the bathroom for the mirror with a decent light, I had to drag along the stand holding the IV. I was still very weak at this point and to do my makeup I had to prop myself against the basin. The IV needle in the vein made it difficult to lift my arm to apply makeup.

One morning the doctor arrived ten minutes earlier than usual. Finding the hospital bed empty, he traced me to the bathroom where he found me propped, wired, and stapled, struggling to draw a line with my eyeliner pencil.

"What on earth are you doing?" he demanded.

I thought it was pretty obvious. But I said, "I am putting on my makeup."

"But you are in a hospital. It's six o'clock in the morning!"

"Look," I told the doctor, "I would put on my eyeliner if I were going to my execution."

No French doctor would have questioned why a female hospital patient was applying her makeup before dawn. A French doctor would have understood that a woman who took care with her appearance would exercise that same care whether she were hospitalized, at a fashionable resort, or on her way to her office. Personal care is something you do *always*.

This is why it is so vital that you have a personal style that is manageable under most circumstances. As I have written in both the original *Chic & Slim* and in *Chic & Slim Encore*, French women's golden rule of chic is "keep it simple." If you design a simple and manageable personal style, you can maintain that personal style on a *toujours*— always—basis.

If you are a mother of young children that require a great deal of your time and mental energy, until they are older and able to do more for themselves, it may be necessary to keep your personal style simpler than later when your children do not require such constant attention.

As for eating moderately and sensibly, the French do this on a consistent basis. If they do partake of one of those multi-course marathon French haute cuisine meals, say at a Michelin three star restaurant , then they are careful to eat lightly for several days before or after. And sometimes both before and after. They always eat moderately and sensibly in each course no matter how many courses are served at the meal. Remember second helpings are considered impolite in France.

I offer you another story about my incorporation of the French Always Principle into my American lifestyle. When you are living among the French, its easier to maintain the practice of eating moderately and sensibly because that is what everyone does. (And I receive email from other women stating that they had no problem eating sensibly in France, but back home in the USA is another matter.)

When I returned to live in the USA, I was attending dinners with family and friends. Especially for holiday dinners when the others were overeating, I was obvious for my restraint. So I decided that on two days each year, Christmas and my birthday, I would allow myself to eat anything and as much as I wanted. The next Christmas, in addition to all the turkey, dressing, cranberry sauce, rolls, and vegetables, I ate three pieces of pie. One with Christmas dinner, one with afternoon tea, and one with supper.

It is impossible to describe to you how miserable with indigestion I became. My body was no longer accustomed to a large quantity of food, particularly such a large quantity of refined sugar that I consumed in those three pieces of pie, one of which was pecan. (I think another was coconut cream.) Sometime around 8:00 PM that evening, I thought I would die of pie. It ruined my Christmas Day.

When my birthday rolled around the next summer, I still ate "anything and as much of it as I wanted." But the quantity of what I wanted was much more reasonable. I was restrained from overeating by not wanting my birthday ruined by indigestion and feeling as miserable as I had on Christmas.

Before we leave the subject of holidays, I want to caution you about overconsumption of alcohol at festive celebrations. My son tells me that, among his generation, even Halloween has become an excuse to drink to excess. Overindulgence in alcohol (at any time) can put a lot of excess sugar calories into your body. Excessive alcohol also weakens your self control. It can destroy all those good intentions to eat moderately and sensibly. I was always impressed at how restrained the French women I knew were in their alcohol consumption. Being intoxicated and silly (and possibly throwing up) is not chic.

If you are making changes in your lifestyle, it will take a while to get your new systems in operation. Do not worry if you are not hitting 100 percent of Always at first. No one is keeping score. This is not the Olympics. This is *your life*. Just do as well as you can, as much of the time as you can.

Gradually your body will become your ally as my body has become my ally. These days if I overeat or if I overindulge in sugar, then I don't have my usual energy level. I find myself avoiding highly sugared items and restricting my quantity of food. I have things to do, and I cannot work efficiently if I am suffering indigestion. I will not have the energy to function efficiently if I overeat or eat the wrong foods.

If I find myself walking with a slouched posture, or chattering when it would have been more in my self-interest to have listened quietly, or doing anything more typical of my fatty life than my improved *Chic & Slim* lifestyle, I spend some time thinking how I might have better handled that situation. I look for opportunities to put myself in a similar situation to practice a positive handling of that situation. I remind myself that the more I do something, the more proficient at it I will become, and the more automatic that action will become for me.

So it is extremely important when you design your personal style that you choose ways of living, eating, and dressing that are possible within your financial and time limitations. So you can achieve that style *always*.

In author Francesca Stanfill's, "Fashion or Folly: In these

trying times, fashion still matters" in the March 2002 *Town & Country,* she reminds us that when a woman *always* takes care of her appearance, it is not out of vanity, but rather self-dignity and courtesy for others.

Francesca Stanfill ends the article telling readers how French designer Coco Chanel believed that a woman should always make herself presentable before she left the house, because "that day she might have a date with destiny. And it's best to be as pretty as possible for destiny." *Toujours.*

How You Do It For Chic & Slim Success:

✎ Whatever defeating habits and practices you have decided to eliminate from your lifestyle, never do them.

✎ Whatever positive, beneficial practices are going to be part of your *Chic & Slim* lifestyle, practice them consistently. Do them *toujours*—always.

Ordering Chic & Slim Books

Chic & Slim books are always available directly from Anne Barone. Order online from *annebarone.com* or by mail order from:

Anne Barone
P.O. Box 3241
Wichita Falls, TX 76301

Mail Order Book Prices:

Chic & Slim (the original) **$10**
Chic & Slim ENCORE **$16**
Chic & Slim TECHNIQUES **$10**

Add **$2** for Shipping (USPS Media Mail) whether ordering one, two, or all three books.

Make check or money order payable to: **Anne Barone**

Chic & Slim books are also sold in select bookstores & dress shops. See *annebarone.com* for a list of these stores and their addresses.

Merci Beaucoup

Sometimes writing and publishing a book is a lot like losing weight. You might, as the ads tease, "lose 30 pounds in 30 days," but most likely the lost pounds would not stay off for the long term. Likewise, I might whip out a new *Chic & Slim* book in a month or two. But most likely the book would not prove useful to you in achieving the kind of chic and slim success you desire. And much thought, much evaluation, and much rewriting and redesigning go into a book that effectively communicates French lifestyle and techniques.

So my first and sincere thanks goes to all the *Chic & Slim* readers who so patiently tolerated the long delays and who sent encouraging email and notes when I was growing increasingly frustrated as a steady stream of unforeseen events delayed completing *Chic & Slim Techniques*.

Looking back more than a decade since I began work on the original *Chic & Slim*, I remember with gratitude so many who have helped my efforts. The initial idea came from my physician Dr. Robert Hillis who kept saying, "You ought to write a book." I did write a book, and now two additional books. *Chic & Slim* has grown from an idea into my life's mission. I am deeply grateful for Dr. Hillis's initial suggestion.

My son John remains my most loyal support. Without his help and without his understanding for his mother's obsession to publish her *Chic & Slim* message, I could never have persevered. The friendship and help of Sheryl and Bob White, Betty Buchanan and Ann Davis has been invaluable.

Hurston Daniel Morris generously donated a wonderful and extensive collection of clippings and books dealing with French women for the *Chic & Slim* background materials library. Mark at Morgan Printing has worked patiently with a novice at book publishing. Stephen has performed magic with the cover files.

The mechanical expertise of Gene Warren of Warren Imports has kept my vehicles in top condition. The crew at the Morningside Station Post Office provides wonderful service for shipping the orders of *Chic & Slim* books. Cynthia Seymour's marketing efforts have boosted *Chic & Slim* book sales.

For this book, *Chic & Slim Techniques*, Joyce Wells turned her practiced teacher's eye on the many errors in my manuscript pages. I have tried to correct all of them. If you still find errors in the book, those errors are mine, not Joyce's.

My prepublication readers provided invaluable advice (and entertaining comments penned in the margins). Some readers agreed to be recognized. Others preferred to remain anonymous. I thank Virginia Bandremer, Cynthia Seymour, and my son John for taking the time to read every word of *Techniques* and make suggestions for its improvement.

Just as surely as the French love good crusty baguettes, I am certain the moment I send this book off to the printers, I will remember others who really, really deserve to be thanked for their help and support.

For all of you, named and unnamed in this acknowledgment, you can take satisfaction that your efforts have enabled many to live healthier, happier, more successful lives, and to develop their own personal styles that are unique — and certainly chic.

My sincerest thanks to all of you. *Merci beaucoup!*

Readers comments are welcome.
Email: anne@annebarone.com
Phone: 940/723-6296
Mailing address: P.O. Box 3241,
Wichita Falls, TX 76301 USA

Be chic, Stay slim!

Anne Barone

chic & slim Success
THE KEY

So where do you start?

Now that you have read the *Chic & Slim* techniques, you may want to try all of them at once. *Non, non! Pas une bonne idée.* Not a good idea.

Those of you familiar with my *Chic & Slim* philosophy know I believe the key to permanent positive change is a gradual approach. Try to change too many eating and lifestyle habits at once, your mind and body will revolt. (That is one reason traditional 'diets' fail.) A gradual approach will also allow your friends and family to adjust to the "new you." They will be less likely to try to sabotage your success because they are uncomfortable with the new person you have become.

So which Technique should you try first?

Seek out *le plaisir*, the pleasure element. Which technique seems to you that it would be the most fun? Which technique is likely to give you a quick sense of accomplishment? Which technique uses only items that you already have on hand? Start with that technique. Then move on to others that seem fun to you. If any of the techniques seem unpleasant, boring, or make you uncomfortable, skip them. You are unlikely to be successful forcing yourself to do something you do not enjoy. Didn't you do enough you did not enjoy back when you were following one "diet" or another?

Some advice: Do not announce that you are doing *Chic & Slim* Techniques. In the first place, that is very un-French. Those chic French women do not talk about living a healthy lifestyle, they just do it. They do not talk about building a chic wardrobe, they just buy or sew the clothes and wear them.

Besides, if you talk about the techniques, you will only be setting yourself up to be bombarded with negativity by tacky, jealous individuals who want you to fail. Remember, if you tell your coworkers that you are trying to improve your eating habits, as soon as you lose two ounces of the 25 pounds your doctor says you should shed, one of those coworkers will start warning you about the dire consequences of anorexia.

More advice: Skip the competition. These techniques are not a sporting event where someone else has defined the rules of the game. Do not compare yourself to others. (Though you can observe others for fashion and lifestyle ideas.) *You* determine your *Chic & Slim* goals. *You* make the decision as to when you have achieved those goals.

More advice: Skip the guilt. If you intended to take 20 minutes to eat your dinner slowly and carefully, and you wolfed it down in seven minutes flat, skip the guilt. Try again next time. Learn the French shrug. A shrug is a marvelous alternative to feeling guilty. Shrugs are French. Guilt is not.

These *Chic & Slim TECHNIQUES* are suggestions, ideas, possibilities, avenues. Tailor these techniques to suit your own lifestyle and your own needs and preferences. Some years ago there was a perfume advertisement featuring a ravishingly chic French woman and the blurb beside her said: "You know enough to make your own rules."

Make your own rules. Enjoy your own unique *Chic & Slim* success.

Bonne chance! Good luck!

Anne Barone